If I Was a Child Again

A collection of memories and
inspirational words from some of Ireland's
finest writers, journalists and TV personalities

Introduction by

Fergus Finlay and Lynda Wilson

Compiled by
Caroline Finnerty

POOLBEG

Published 2013
by Poolbeg Press Ltd
123 Grange Hill, Baldoyle
Dublin 13, Ireland
E-mail: poolbeg@poolbeg.com
www.poolbeg.com

The moral right of the author has been asserted.

1

A catalogue record for this book is available from the British Library.

ISBN 978-1-84223-600-0

Typeset by Poolbeg Press Ltd in Sabon 11.5/15.5

Printed and bound by CPI Group (UK) Ltd, Croydon, CR0 4YY

www.poolbeg.com

Contents

Introduction

First of all, all of us in Barnardos, in Northern Ireland and the Republic, are really grateful to Poolbeg Press for doing it again! Last year's Christmas book was brilliant, and it is wonderful that once again so many writers have given their time, their talent, and either their imaginations or their memories, to put this smashing collection together.

If you ask most of us the question, "What would you do if you were a child again for a day?", it would immediately spark off a jumble of memories in all our heads – and maybe get a great conversation going around the dinner table. The things we didn't do and always wanted to, and things we did that maybe we shouldn't have. (One of us – we won't say who – can still remember being part of a gang that was chased for miles by a very cross farmer whose orchard we had just emptied!)

But nowadays we work with children who might not want to ever revisit their own childhoods. We work as hard as possible to give all our children, when we're working with them, the best possible childhood we can. And we worry when they go home about the neighbourhoods they live in, or the cold and damp houses, or the problems in the families. Sometimes we think the best thing we can do for our children is to help them build their resilience, because life throws all sorts of adversity their way.

Helping children to get the most out of school, helping to build their confidence, to give them a strong sense of who they are and why they're important, helping them to make better choices in their lives (especially when the bad choices are easier) – it might sound simple, but actually it's painstaking work.

It involves building close and honest relationships with

children and their families. It takes time and effort. There are setbacks, and sometimes very small increments of progress. If you really want to change the lives of children for the better, you have to decide right from the start that you won't give up.

And the people who work in Barnardos never give up! It can be emotionally demanding for the staff who work with children in disadvantage every day. But if you feel at the end of the day that you've helped someone to look back on a childhood that was happier and more fulfilling than it might have been otherwise, that's truly rewarding.

In the times we live in, the need for that work is greater than it has ever been. But the resources available are squeezed tighter and tighter all the time. That's why we really appreciate the support a book like this can give.

We know from talking to some of the writers in this collection that they all got a huge kick out of reliving a moment of childhood. And we hope that everyone who buys the book will enjoy the experience just as much. By putting this collection together, and by getting it to the top of the bestseller lists hopefully, Poolbeg Press, and all the writers here, and all of you who have bought the book are all helping, each in your own way, to change a child's life for the better.

Fergus Finlay
Chief Executive
Barnardos (Republic of Ireland)

Lynda Wilson
Director
Barnardo's Northern Ireland

The Daisy Bell Summers

Claire Allan

I don't know how old it actually was. It seemed ancient. "A boneshaker," my granddad called it as he wheeled it in to show me.

"A Daisy Bell!" the children on the street laughed and teased – I didn't understand the local nick-name, but it didn't sound as though a "Daisy Bell" was a good thing.

But there it was – and it was mine: this bike which my daddy and my granddad had lovingly restored and sprayed silver and handed to me.

I'd never had my very own bike before – I just had a few hand-me-downs over the years: my aunt's old bike and a marvellously massive trike that we (all four of us) loved and fought over. The Silver Daisy Bell, as it will always be known, felt like mine – all mine – in that no one in my family had ever owned her before or was allowed to ride her.

It was tall, thin – the tyres skinny and the wheels maybe a little bit shaky – the brakes were pretty suspect too – but that Daisy Bell was the key to my freedom. When I sat on my bike I felt as if I was towering above everyone else on a penny-farthing – but it didn't matter. I loved that bike from the

1

minute it was rolled into our garden and presented to me.

This was 1980s Derry – where no one had much but, as the song says, we saw it through without complaining.

It feels like a different world – a hazy, sepia-toned world of long sunny days and sun-blistered pavements, and the Daisy Bell that everyone else laughed at but I loved as if it was a top-of-the-range Raleigh with a basket and bell.

In my childhood I would pretend the Daisy Bell was a car – my car. And every time I sat on that hard saddle, I would imagine I was driving.

We covered some serious miles together – when I think of it now, I couldn't imagine letting my children away with the same sense of freedom we had. But although Northern Ireland in the eighties was less than ideal in a lot of ways, it was still a different world and there existed an innocence of childhood that we lapped up as we explored the world around us.

Every weekend, and each day of the summer holidays, my sister (just one year older), my aunt (just three years older) and I would set off on an adventure. With a tinny transistor radio in the basket of my aunt's bike, and a bottle of well-diluted Kia-Ora we would head out the "back roads" – the country lanes which led from Derry to Donegal. If we were particularly lucky we would have managed to scramble together a few pence to buy a packet of Custard Creams in the Spar shop, which would be our picnic once we reached our destination.

We pushed our bikes up impossibly steep hills, and freewheeled back down them – passing fields in a flurry of childhood excitement. The sun would beat down – but of course you didn't wear sun-cream in those days. I don't think we'd ever heard of it. And as for safety helmets and knee-pads, and any sense of real road awareness, none seemed to exist.

When you were on the back roads, you rarely if ever came across a car. The roads were our own.

Halfway on our journey we reached "The Dragon's Teeth" – large concrete blocks that separated the North from the South. As army checkpoints could not exist on every road, the simple way to deal with controlling the flow of traffic was to erect these concrete bollards that jutted from the road. They didn't really look like teeth but often I would allow myself to imagine that they were just that. It added to the mystique of the adventure – winding roads and a dragon's teeth.

And the Banshee. *Darby O'Gill and the Little People* has an awful lot to answer for. It's a film we watched as children – and harmless and all as it seemed, once the notion of the Banshee was put in your head it was hard to shift.

There was this one stretch, on the road to our destination, where the trees overgrew and no matter how sunny the day it always felt cold. And if you listened hard enough you could make out the howl of the wind. I'm not ashamed to say it would on occasion give me the bad fear and I would speed up the peddling on my bike to get through that dark recess as quickly as possible while promising to the Lord our God, with all the piousness typical of a ten-year-old, that I would never steal another biscuit out of the jar if He kept every one of my family safe from harm.

In this life, they say, we all have mountains to climb. In my childhood, on my silver Daisy Bell, this was more than accurate. The destination of our jaunts out each day was always Grianán of Aileach – an ancient Irish ring fort at the top of an exceptionally steep hill, which watches over the four corners of Inishowen and Derry. We never even attempted to cycle up that hill, which winds its way around the mountain for more than a mile. Cars struggled on that hill on a good day – so instead, switching off the transistor radio, we would gird our loins, take a deep breath and set off pushing our bikes up that hill singing "I Have Confidence" from *The Sound of Music* as loud as we could as we went.

I'm not sure we knew all the words but we gave it the best shot we could, feeling our confidence growing with each step we took closer to the top. And when we reached that summit – what a sight would we behold! It felt as if we were looking out over the whole of Ireland.

There was quiet calm inside the ring fort at Grianán. If you stood in the one spot for long enough, closed your eyes and listened intently, you could almost hear the echoes of every person who had stood there over hundreds of years. I felt that, even as a child. It was there in our bones: the feel of the place, the calmness – broken only then by the rattling of the Custard Cream packet and the pouring of the Kia-Ora into plastic tumblers or the sounds of tourists chatting and marvelling at the ancient structure.

We would climb the steps, which felt perilously high, and sit on the edge of the wall – aware that one false move could send us tumbling to the ground. We were never scared of it. We thrived on it.

And when we climbed back down, we would crouch and climb into the tiny tunnels – remembering distant stories about fairy keeps and wishing chairs.

Still fresh in my mind is the time we saw baby mice, reminiscent of baked beans – bald, pink, small, wriggling – in the gateway. I'm not sure I was ever as keen on crawling through the tunnels after that. Our trips gave me confidence but they never quite took away my fear of mice!

Our return journeys were mighty *craic*. Not least because the biggest pay-off for pushing our bikes up that blasted mountainside was the ride, freewheeling, back down it. This was exhilarating, terrifying and hilarious. With every return journey I prayed the ancient brakes on the Daisy Bell would save me from oblivion – at the same time enjoying the rush of the wind through my hair and the screams of joy as we let go and enjoyed the ride.

The hills were faster on the way back. The sun shone brighter. The corner where I was sure the Banshee lived was still very much there and very frightening – but I peddled fast past it and tried not to think of that scene in *Darby O'Gill* where the coachman bids him to "Get in".

We would pass the Dragon's Teeth and the Spar shop and cross the reservoir over to home and then once there we would stop, maybe grab a sandwich and let our parents know we were okay and ponder what to do with the rest of our day.

The answer was simple. We would head out again. We would refill the Kia-Ora and check how many Custard Creams we had left and on we would cycle – back out to Grianán all over again.

We never seemed to get tired. Our legs never ached. We never got bored with the journey. We found magic and good *craic* every time we went. I always imagined the dragons laying low beneath the roads, the fairies dancing at the ring fort and the Banshee in waiting.

And the Daisy Bell – painted silver and old and rattley – never did let me down.

It wasn't the fanciest bike on the street. It was far from cool. It didn't make anyone jealous. No one admired it. No one envied me. But that bike was my most prized possession bar none and in the company of my sister and aunt we enjoyed so many happy adventures together.

Would I do it again if I could? Relive those hazy moments on my precious bike, with my precious friends? Yes. I would. I can almost taste the Kia-Ora if I think about it long enough.

Claire Allan is a Derry-based journalist and author of seven novels, including *Rainy Days and Tuesdays*, *What Becomes of the Broken Hearted?* and *The First Time I Said Goodbye*. She is a mother of two (one of each) and is a Twitter addict. Her childhood was made particularly special by her wonderful parents Peter and Karen, her grandparents, sisters and brother, auntie Marie-Louise and cousins from England, Denis and Tracey. She would really like to own another bike one day – but she's not brave enough after a spin class made her cry.

An Accident of Birth?

Jennifer Barrett

I still remember the piercing pain. I can't have been more than five years old, but that ear infection was so sore that it is forever etched in my memory.

My mother put some ear drops into my throbbing ear and gave me a Disprin dissolved in a glass of orange squash; then she took me in her arms, covered my sore ear with her hand and cuddled me until the medication started to take effect. As my tears abated, she gently drew pictures on my face with the tip of her finger. And just as I began to drift off, I remember her whispering that she loved me more than anything in the world.

I opened one eye. "Really?"

"Yes, you and your brothers are so precious to me," she said, "I wouldn't swap you for all the money in the world."

This fully woke me from my drowsy state. It seemed somewhat suspect to me. I mean, my brothers and I were great 'n' all – but not for *all* the money in the world! This needed clarification.

"Not even for a hundred pounds?" I asked, placing the largest denomination of funds I could possibly imagine on the table. Times were difficult growing up in 1970s Ireland, and I was always aware that money was tight. I wouldn't have blamed my mother if she'd given in under such enormous temptation – it was a whole *hundred* pounds after all.

But my mother just smiled, kissed my forehead, squeezed me a little tighter and began to hum the tune of "Danny Boy". I drifted off to sleep safe in the knowledge that we were all to remain poor, but happy together for a very long time to come.

I am blessed that my childhood was packed full of such tender moments and memories – I wouldn't change a single thing about it. I remember long, happy, fun-filled summer days on Brittas Bay beach with my siblings and cousins, and walks in the countryside with my mum, dad, brothers and the much-loved pooch of the time – whether it was Sam, Oscar or Harvey, all very much a part of our noisy family life. And I can easily recall the joy in the house as each new bonny Barrett baby joined the brood: my younger brother Chris, his two little legs in plaster for his early months to help turn his feet out the right way; changing nappies for my cute little sister Suz as she giggled and smiled, charming everyone she met (including her big sis). I even look back with fondness at the daily squabbles and scrapes between me and my older brother Paul. The poor fella didn't know what hit him when his wilful little sister arrived, and our squabbles toughened me up for life ahead.

But I almost didn't make it at all – when my mother was just three months pregnant with me, the doctor told her that there was a strong possibility that I wouldn't make it. But she was having none of it. Determined I would survive, she took to the bed and rested up for a month while my father and grandmother looked after my older brother and the house. And I obviously enjoyed being closely minded – so much so that I didn't want to come out at all in the end . . . Eventually, several weeks late, but in the fullness of health, and by all accounts a pudgy thing with a shock of dark hair, I took my first breaths. I was born at home with a midwife as was the popular trend in England at the time, so my father was right there to witness my birth. Apparently I had excellent timing, arriving quite quickly in the end on

Saturday morning at ten o'clock, leaving plenty of time for Dad to go on to cook a roast dinner for my visiting grandparents and our little family. But in all the excitement of the new arrival, Dad forgot to defrost the chicken before roasting it, and on my every birthday until the day she died my grandmother enjoyed teasing him about that iced roast chicken meal.

So, once my mum was back in charge of the cooking, my childhood was always safe, secure and happy. But there are times I wonder how much of my good fortune was down to nothing more than a twist of fate, a small accident of birth? What if I hadn't arrived into that terraced house in Croydon to Maureen and John? I was late after all and, according to some, not even expected to make it at all. So what if I'd arrived somewhere else entirely? If I were a child again, and born somewhere else, to different parents – how different might my childhood, my life, have been?

Not long ago my work took me to a small project run by Australian missionary Brothers in the Kibera Slum in Nairobi, Kenya. Kibera has some of the harshest living conditions I have ever witnessed. Almost one million people live there in an area roughly the same size as Central Park in New York. It is an extremely poor area and most of its inhabitants lack access to basic facilities such as electricity or a fresh water supply. Small children play on large mounds of rubbish, sewage and scrap; broken-down cars drive along mud-tracks lined by small tin-shack shops, the many gaps in roofs and windows patched up with cardboard boxes and plastic sacks. The houses are built in winding mazes, spiralling up and down the mud hills. As you walk through the narrow lanes, you need to dodge low under protruding, corrugated-iron structures – most of which my mother would have said could have plucked your eye out – and in this case she would have been right. I dread to think what conditions are like in the rainy season when the ground underneath must be slippy and dangerous.

Certainly no place for a child to grow up.

You would think . . .

Yet it was here that I visited the Mary Rice Centre – a small special-needs school and centre. It is a tiny but vibrant place offering these often forgotten children physical therapy and a chance at education, the ultimate goal being to help them make the transition into state schools.

As the school was closed for holidays, we visited some of the children and their families in their homes. Isaac, a child with cerebral palsy was living in a newly built multi-storey building on the outskirts of the slum. Arriving at the complex, I was dismayed to see a pile of rubbish and sewage out front almost half as high as the building itself. There were no lifts inside, and I wondered how this family managed to carry their severely disabled child up the ten flights of stairs to their fifth-storey flat each day. I marvelled at what genius could have decided to give this family this flat, and not one on the ground floor that Isaac could access with greater ease in his wheelchair. I felt dismayed for this poor young boy and his family, and uneasy about my own comparably privileged situation. How could it be right that I could have so much, could be given such a good start in life, while here on the other side of the world a young boy must contend with poverty and physical challenge on a scale that I could barely begin to comprehend.

But once inside, my view changed. The flat was small and minimally furnished, but utterly spotless. I was introduced to Isaac's maternal grandmother and aunt who were looking after him while his own mother was attending a funeral. African women are truly remarkable in how they come together to support and help each other rear their families. The women led me to a small room where Isaac was waiting to meet me. As soon as he saw them his eyes lit up. They embraced, and I sat beside Isaac. He didn't talk, but he didn't need to – his smile was as broad as any I've seen. Pride and love shone in the eyes of his family, who delighted in his every movement. We talked about their lives, which were certainly very hard, but I learnt how as a family they all pulled together to ensure Isaac had the best life that they could give him, and about how important the Mary

Rice Centre was to the whole family. And as we spoke Isaac smiled, took my hand, put on my sunglasses for a photograph, played with my charm bracelet, and tried on the hat I was holding – charming me just as he obviously had his own extended family. And I realised that this was a strong family unit no different from my own. There was no need for me to feel sorry for Isaac. He may have severe physical challenges, and his family had little materially, but he was rich in the love and support of his family, and through the Centre he also had a chance of education and much-needed physical therapy for his condition. He was a genuinely happy young boy – glowing with happiness, in fact. The experience changed my view of the world.

Just a few years earlier in Ireland, and affected by my experience as a volunteer with the Special Olympics 2003 World Games in Ireland, I volunteered at a local social project. Every Wednesday a disco and club was held where adults with special needs could dance, socialise with friends, and play pool, darts and other games. It was here that I met Vincent. If you didn't know Vincent, at first you might not realise he had special needs at all. It was only after talking to him for a while that you realised he was a little slow – but just a little. A gentle soul, he preferred to have one-on-one chats with the volunteers and older club members than to join in with any of the noisier group activities. I remember one conversation when Vincent asked me if I had my own car. When I said I did, he appeared quite sad and wistful for a moment, before telling me that it was his dream to drive a car. Then he asked if I had a mobile phone. And when I showed him my phone, he smiled and told me that his aunt was buying him one for his birthday in a couple of months. He was so excited about having his first phone that he told me about it again every week that we met.

On club nights, we would sing "Happy Birthday" to whoever was celebrating their birthday that week. I hadn't told anyone there the date of my birthday, but a few days after it we sang happy birthday to Vincent. That was when Vincent and I worked out that we were born just one day apart. Just one day, and another accident of birth separated me and this sensitive, thoughtful young man who could only dream of driving a car, and whose year was made when he finally got his own mobile phone. It struck me that so much that I take for granted was aspirational to this young man who just one day later was born into a different situation to me – his mind just ever so slightly different from mine.

So if I were a child again, but this time born into a different place, family or situation – perhaps one like Isaac's or Vincent's, life would doubtless be hard. But who am I to judge whether that childhood, that life, would be better or worse than my own? All we ever know is our own reality, our own existence. With the love and security of our own family and people, and the added support of vital services in our community, every child has a chance of happiness.

Just like everyone else, today Vincent is a young man struggling with the cards life dealt him, but he is a happy, sociable fellow who delights in the small things of life that might seem of little importance to others. And the day that I met Isaac in Nairobi he seemed just as happy and content in his supportive family unit as I had done that day when my mother reassured me she wouldn't give me up for all the money in the world.

I just wonder what might have happened if I'd offered her a *thousand* pounds though?

Jennifer Barrett is chief executive of a developing world charity, and over the years has worked in a number of fundraising, marketing and development roles across a range of Irish arts organisations, schools, colleges and other non-profit organisations. She divides her time between her home in West Dublin and her busy family home in Wicklow where her large family descend most weekends. A keen photographer, she spends much of her spare time travelling far and wide to photograph and observe whales and other marine life in their natural habitats. It was a particularly magical experience with orcas in the arctic waters of Norway that inspired her first novel *Look into the Eye*, published by Poolbeg Press.

Back to the Future

Shirley Benton

"If you were a child again, would you do anything differently knowing what you know now?" Michael Parkinson asks me.

(Disclaimer: I do not know Michael Parkinson. However, it is two in the morning as I think about this and there's just something weird about walking around the house asking yourself questions. Obviously, if you pretend you're being interviewed by Michael Parkinson, there's absolutely nothing weird about that at all.)

"Well, Parky," I reply (because, feck it, he seems like a decent sort and we might as well be good pals – do it properly or don't do it at all, I say) "that's an interesting question. I suppose now that I think about it, plenty of the issues we battle against as adults go back to childhood . . . take sweets, for example. They might make you fat and rot your teeth but I *love* the blasted things, and I think I'm not being bigheaded when I say they love me right back. But when did this love affair begin? When I was a kid."

And after thirty-something years of loving sweets, there will probably never be a day when I won't feel compelled to do jumping jacks in the ad breaks of TV shows, or to park my car a mile away from the shopping centre and walk there and back in the rain just to get a bit of exercise in. To be honest with you, I could live without all of that. But giving up sweets now as a solution . . . nah. It'd be like the death of a much-loved family pet who managed to live for thirty-odd years – a medical aberration of a pet, yes, but much loved nonetheless. No, it's too extreme and life's hard enough. It's just a pity I ever went near the damn things in the first place.

"So if you could turn the clock back, you'd never have had that first sweet?" Parky asks me.

I open my mouth to confirm that I wouldn't. And then, slowly, I close it again. *Wouldn't* I?

You see, rightly or wrongly, lots of the recollections that live in my happy-memories-of-childhood box seem to involve the sugary stuff: the bag of pick 'n' mix my granny would place in my outstretched hands when she came up to ours of a Sunday night just before *Where in the World?*, which couldn't be confiscated by a parent because Granny gave it and what Granny said went; the planning that went into the buying of the penny sweets and rolls of stickers in Molly Burke's on Main Street, Toomevara; the anticipation of candyfloss (a substance I would have sold a kidney for on dreary Mondays when it was bacon-and-cabbage-dinner day) on the rare occasions when the circus came to town. I don't know if the pleasure derived came from the sweets themselves or the overall happy-vibe scenarios, but I do know that those memories would have been impossible without them. So no, maybe we'll leave the sweets alone.

"Ah, I wouldn't go that far now."

Parky's giving me a dubious look. Time to steer the conversation elsewhere before the interrogation begins.

"You know what I'd change, actually? I'm a terrible hoarder, and my mother told me that began around the age of six. I'd keep single Sindy Doll shoes even if I'd lost the other shoe down the street taking the dolls for a walk – someone might have called to the door with it a few months after or something, you know how it is in small villages – and *Jackie* magazines that had been published four years previously, that kind of thing. God, I loved my *Buntys* and my *Jackies* – it would have been criminal to throw them away when I had more than enough time on my hands to reread them. There was a time when I could neither get in to or out of my bedroom because of the piles of magazines stored behind the door, and I had to come and go through the window – that was kind of funny actually, looking back on it –"

"You think?"

"Em . . . no, no. I'm joking, of course."

I'm not.

"Of course."

I always thought you were friendlier than this on the television, I can't help thinking.

"So if someone could have waved a magic wand over your six-year-old self, would you have wished for the gift of tidiness?" he asks.

Here's where we're going to fall out. "Oh, I was always *tidy*, Parky. I knew where everything was – I just had a lot of it, that's all. And I can assure you, any free carpet space was spotless."

"Sure, sure. How many inches would that have been, do you think?"

I glower at him.

"Okay, let me rephrase. So you wish you'd been the kind of child that threw out, say, their colouring books when they'd finished them?"

"God, no. Do you not remember how nice it was to look back over all the colouring you'd done?"

"I . . . can't say I do, no."

"You haven't lived, Parky."

He gives me a look that suggests he's not the one who's guilty of that. But I bet he doesn't have a collection of vintage Kellogg's Cornflakes bicycle-spoke reflectors from the eighties. Or a stack of Telecom Éireann CallCards. And I do. *Hah!*

"Anything else, Shirley? Say, if you had one day to be a child again, what exactly would you do?"

17

I think about the things that are really affecting my life now – things that, unlike a fondness for sweets or a penchant for keeping things longer than I should, I can't do much about because it's too late. I think about the things that are affecting the lives of those around me, both people I know and people I don't, and wonder if there is anything I could do on my one day of life as a child again that would make a difference. And I suddenly visualise myself going back to the late eighties (admittedly I'd be a rather old child then, but I'd also be at the age to exercise a level of articulation that our younger selves don't have) and, like The Ghost of Christmas Future, visiting the political leaders of that time and telling them exactly what was to come. What their legacy would be. Because, to my mind, the foundations of what our country now is, what it stands for, were laid down long ago and built upon by others following their example. What did we learn from being 'the sick man of Europe' in the 1980s recession? From the brain drain that inevitably resulted from that decade's unemployment levels? From the sense of stagnation felt by those who remained? What did every single person who was in charge of our country from the post-recession period onwards do to ensure that our nation would not end up in this situation again if we somehow found ourselves with money to do something with? Why did we go into the boom of the late nineties with such a blinkered, greedy vision of spend, spend, spend rather than saving our extra money?

It's not that simple, of course. A considerable portion of our economic woes can be attributed to a global jigsaw of problems. But if you were to say to anyone on the street that we as a country did all we could to help ourselves before the inevitable day when it would all come crashing down, that we kept our house in order while times were good, you'd be hard pressed to find someone to agree with you. The man whose mother is currently on a trolley in a hospital corridor, still waiting to be seen after eight hours, flicking through a newspaper full of details on the latest banking scandal to distract himself from his family's hardship, wouldn't. The overworked hospital worker doing the job of several people wouldn't either. The person walking to the supermarket to save money on petrol, who's wondering how much longer it'll be before her family home is repossessed, would laugh at you if you said that to her. Issues like drastic cuts in healthcare-spending personally impacting people's lives, negative equity and a consignment to pay a mortgage on a house in a ghost estate that will never be finished, and an inability to pay bills at the end of the month due to cumulative mortgage-interest-rate hikes – the kind of issues that have my fellow countrymen awake at two o'clock in the morning for reasons other than being a night owl like myself – are almost normal to us now. A level of personal responsibility is demanded from all of us, but the buck has to stop with someone. We were not the experts, yet we are the ones to pay. If those in power knew then what we know now, would someone – anyone – have done anything differently? If they were given an understanding of the undercurrent of anger that pervades 2013 Ireland, would anyone have cared enough to put reasoned measures in place to prevent, or at the very least alleviate, the current pressure on this country's inhabitants?

Sadly, I'm not convinced that anything any child could have said would have made a difference. Instead, I would probably have been better off to tell myself, and every other kid, to just enjoy that 99 with extra sprinkles and syrup before we all developed dairy allergies or swore off cones because we know now just how many calories they contain. I would tell myself never to leave a snowball fight just because there's homework to be done, because the evening is long and the homework will always be there but the snow won't. Neither will the years, the time or the inclination. As I grew older and more aware, I would remind myself to try to be appreciative of having someone paying for the house I lived in, because the day might come when I'm paying mad money for a house that's worth half the price it was when I bought it. It would be no harm to appreciate the fact too that someone else was running the house I lived in, because one day I would fully comprehend just how much work goes into that. I would try to understand that it was never going to be that simple again and that I should just live in the moment. That I might think it's complicated, but really, it's not. I would add that, further down the line, that guy from the neighbouring area was *so* not worth it.

Parky's looking at me. He's expecting an answer.

"Do you know, Parky, I think I'd get a nice big bag of sweets and an armful of old magazines and sit down and relax for the day."

I prepare myself for the confused look.

He sits forward in his seat. Then he smiles.

"As things to do go, that's as good as any."

Shirley Benton is originally from the metropolis of Toomevara in Tipperary but now lives in Dublin with her husband and children. She studied English and French as part of her BA degree in Mary Immaculate College of Education, Limerick, and completed a postgraduate Diploma in Systems Analysis in NUI Galway. After working full-time in IT for ten years, she left the industry in 2009 to pursue her dream of becoming a writer whilst working part-time as a freelance editor and proofreader. She has had two books published by Poolbeg: *Looking for Leon* and *Can We Start Again?*. She is also a book reviewer for the chicklit website www.chicklitclub.com, and contributes author interviews and writing-related articles to its associated blog, *Connect*. She is a lover of the Irish language and when she is not writing or reviewing, she can be found on her couch watching TG4, if you're looking for her.

Kick the Can

Siobháin Bunni

It's the summer of 1979. I could probably pick any day that summer; they were, in my memory, mostly good days. Great days. It seemed hotter back then, like rain didn't exist and every summer day was a blistering one. The sun, fighting its way through the thick leafy canopy of chestnut trees that line the gently sloping driveway. A sea breeze, weakened but still fresh from its journey to cool our flushed little faces. The smell of the fresh-cut grass and the sound of sneezing noses it tickled. The tiered lawn, dry and hard enough to hurt, surrounded by all of those first-rate hiding places gifted by a garden so overgrown and wild with bushes, trees and shrubs.

Presiding over this great playground, the house stands majestic if a little sombre with its burnt red brick set into white render contrasting with the black slate roof that slopes over the beautiful residence: a strong, solid house with white-painted timber sash windows that rattle and moan in the wind. It smells like home. It is home.

In the heart of the garden reigns the laburnum tree, as bright as the sun in early summer, a dripping crown of sunny yellow blossoms draped protectively over the turn in the driveway, and the heart of our imagination. Depending on the day, the game and the players this sprawling tree is a house, a shop, a swing or a school, but today it is The Can, and today we're all in.

Excited shrieks pierce this warm summer day, accompanied by the fast flurry of feet on the driveway, first one pair then two as they belt furiously towards the tree.

Only five of us then – it would be a few years yet before our "little princess" would join us but, none the wiser, we accepted an honorary sixth in the shape of our neighbour – as good as one of us. We were then two boys and four girls, but you couldn't really rely on the youngest, because she could just about run, never mind hide. Even my older sister played that day, not too distracted by her *Jackie* magazines or Cliff Richard miming some happy-chappy melody on *Top of the Pops*, to join in. She'll kill me for saying this, but when she wasn't looking after us, she loved to sit and swoon over his quiffy hair and handsome 1970s' smooth pretty-boy face.

"*Kick the Can! I spy Layla behind Mum's car!*"

She, the youngest, was always seen but never caught first: the game would die otherwise as she would then be the next "It". What good is the game without a race, the odds stacked against her and her unsteady, slow but adorable little-girl run with her golden locks jiggling behind her? But good to get her out fairly soon, we agreed – too young to count, too cute to exclude. We took this game very seriously, the challenging highlight of every summer.

Oh, the excitement at having found a new never-been-used-before hiding place, the disappointment at needing to give it up to go pee.

It is a game of hard-knuckle wits, to sit it out and watch, like a sniper. To bide your time and wait. To hold off until the seeker passes you by or strays sufficiently from The Can, lured by spying a protruding arm or an exposed leg or a peeping shoe. Then, when far enough away, the risk of leaving your hiding place to sneak slowly at first, creeping silently forward then dash with an adrenaline-pumping roar at the top of your voice.

"Kick the Can, I free all!"

Oh, the joy: to reach that tree first. To dive at the thick trunk and feel the first touch of rough bark at your fingers. The howl of encouragement and the air-punching leap of victory.

Likely we played until we couldn't run any more, till our voices gave up or until a fight broke out amidst accusations of cheating as someone was glimpsed lurking darkly in the glazed porch. Hiding inside the house was always out of bounds, but too much of a draw to resist regardless of the punishing game-evicting consequences. Either way the day was thirst-quenchingly good and probably ended with gulps of lukewarm water and dinner al fresco, my mum in her brown-and-orange kaftan with the flowing sleeves and hair pulled back in a wide matching hair-band and Dad sporting a dapper cravat and slacks. If we were lucky he might be pulling on a sherry-soaked cigar and we could all get drunk on the sweet-smelling fumes.

We are together. United. Innocent. Happy on those days in our own company.

If I could go back to that time, for just one day, I would exploit my memory of the best spot we ever found and hide out to ultimately win the last game of the day – well, the trip back in time has to reap some selfish benefit! Then I would do nothing more than sit on that makeshift swing suspended from our yellow play tree, breathe deep and savour the moment, the laughs and the excitement. I would soak up the feeling and relive the moment where we were comrades together.

The simplicity. The innocence. Where our only worry was who stole our socks, who was rooting in our various rooms, what was for dinner or what trouble we were in when Dad got home from work after our day of high jinks, with his enormous weighted hands and fiery temper. For each of us, although me more often than not, the fearful words "You just wait till your father gets home!", often shrieked in frustration, made our hearts quiver and knees tremble. My mother at the end of her tether. The consequential wait for the clockwork arrival of our dad at seven on the dot and without fail was torture. Would she tell or would she soften? A game of chance, often lost, rarely won. As Dad approached from his long drive home we could hear the purr of the engine as it descended the hill and pace its progress from the noise it made gearing down to turn its nose into the drive. And as it glided over the final few metres up the drive to turn and stop just outside the sitting-room window, I would retreat to the top of the stairs and listen out for the telltale mumbling and the eventual roar.

"*Siobháinnnnnnn!*"

And I knew I was done for. No softening today then.

It was never anything really bad. Just something really, really bold. A scrap with one of the sisters. An instruction disobeyed. A display of bad temper or cheek. As I got older, though, the boldness got a little bit wilder: missed curfews, stealing sweets from the local shop, sneaking out after bed to go to the Summit disco. And so a stint at a secluded finishing school for young ladies put an abrupt halt to my gallop. My mother says now that my eldest daughter, so headstrong and spirited, is her revenge on me. And I am both delighted and scared. I don't know where she gets it from . . .

So my journey back for just one day would be to one of those days that summertime because after that things started to get complicated and the livin' wasn't so easy.

But there would be no quiet "in hindsight" inciteful whispers of inspiration to my young self. No secret words of warning or caution – knowing me then as I do now, I probably wouldn't listen anyway, not even to myself – no clues or watch-outs-for-things-to-come.

I might give a gentle nod to my brother to avoid diving on his homemade rope swing above the rockery and save him a serious bloody gash to the back of his head. And I would definitely give particular counsel to my younger sister to be cautious in her future romantic dalliances, without freaking her out, if she'd understand. And out of divilment I might warn my neighbour of the harmless crush I would develop on him a couple of years later, but that would be it. Because what comes next is what makes us who we are, and who am I to influence that? They might not all be the great experiences or events that we'd hope for, and some are ones we'd rather not have; the ones that hurt us most are often the ones that shape us most. But collectively, combined with the persuasive events and positive encounters, they become the ingredients that flavour us and determine our futures. Who am I to decide what my siblings could or should be? And despite my flaws, and I have quite a few, I'm content, if a little challenged, by who I am.

So for me the moment would be about enjoying the carefree togetherness of my siblings. A wish to have our innocence back for just one more day. The innocence of ignorance and the bliss of a warm summer's day, screaming for all the right reasons.

Born in 1968 in Baghdad, Iraq, Siobháin Bunni is one of six children born to her Irish mother and Iraqi father. A rebellious young lady, she was educated in Kylemore Abbey in Connemara before graduating from the College of Marketing & Design, with an Advanced Diploma in Environmental Design. Married to Ross since 1997 following a romantic elopement to the Amalfi Coast in Italy, they have three beautiful children, a boy and two girls. Together they live in Malahide, Co Dublin. Until recently she worked as a design manager with Eason & Son Ltd where she managed the development of the design of the new flagship stores and has now started a new contract as Interim Brand and Communications manager with Vodafone.

Daydream Believer

Jennifer Burke

I'd like to say I was a dreamer as a child. But really I was just a daydreamer, which is something else altogether. A dreamer sits and imagines the future stretching ahead, full of possibilities. On the other hand, a daydreamer like me stares into space, seeing not what is in front of them, but an imagined world where adventures come alive. One benefit of daydreaming is that whereas a dreamer's fantasies are limited to earthly realities, anything, from time travel to fairy tales, can manifest themselves in a daydreamer's mind.

"It's so great that you've qualified as a solicitor," a relative said to me, after the event. She elaborated that apparently I was such a daydreamer as a child there had been a worry I wouldn't be able to stick to anything concrete! But I kept the stories going inside my head and, this year, the daydream came true and my first novel was published.

A question I've been asked a number of times since news leaked out about my book deal is: "How long have you been writing?"

The answer is simply, "For as long as I can remember." So I have already spent some time this year reminiscing about my childhood, and how I always loved to write. Recently, I stumbled across an old copybook of stories from my early years in primary school. I read one of them, eager to see if my literary leanings had shown promise at a young age. Ahem. It was no Man Booker prequel, I can tell you that! It started as follows: "*My name is Jennifer. I love my Mammy. I love my Daddy. My best friend is Maeve. I love Maeve. My teacher is Miss Joyce. I love Miss Joyce.*" I could go on, but I think you get the gist.

But I did progress from factual statements to plot-driven excerpts after a while. During my obsession with Enid Blyton's "The Secret Seven" and "The Famous Five", I developed a series entitled "The Nice Nine". In hindsight, I could have picked "The Nasty Nine" or "The Exciting Eleven" but I was a Care Bears kid and, until the age of seven, was content with calm and quiet. Little did I know that life as I knew it was about to change.

At this stage, I should probably reveal that my newly published novel, *The Secret Son*, is not my first success. I had already tasted the heady word of literary fame at the tender age of ten.

It all started three years earlier when my parents took me to dinner in the "64" restaurant at the top of Gorey town (I remember every detail) to make an announcement.

"I'm pregnant!" Mum said, beaming.

"What does pregnant mean?"

"We're going to have a baby!"

I can still remember the feeling that bubbled through me on hearing those words – I thought I was going to burst with excitement. I was an only child until I was seven. All my friends had brothers and sisters. I had wanted one for so long and finally, finally, he was on his way!

I was a relatively patient child, but even by my standards the next few months were torture. I wanted him born *now*! In the absence of satisfaction, I contented myself with preparing as best I could. I picked up the post for Mum when she became too big to bend down. I made lists upon lists of boys' and girls' names –

stealing some from my favourite books at the time. But my parents probably made the right decision in vetoing Br'er Bear and Br'er Rabbit. I don't think my now twenty-three-year-old brother would have appreciated it.

Finally, the due date arrived. I left school for my Easter holidays, promising to return with news of a little brother or sister. "Well," my teacher and classmates raced up to me on our first day back, "is it a boy or a girl?" I wanted to cry. The stupid kid still hadn't been born and in the end was thirteen days late. I felt very hard done by, although in hindsight it was my Mum who deserved the sympathy.

But he couldn't stay put forever. I remember being dropped off with our neighbours, Séamus and Angela, while my parents raced off to hospital. I sat in the bed they made up for me, staring out the window at the street lamps lighting the dark estate, wondering if he had been born yet. The next morning, I was preoccupied with my breakfast (Séamus and Angela didn't have my usual cereal and I was wondering how I could get out of eating what they gave me) when there was a loud knock on the door. Séamus opened it, and I'll never forget the smile on my dad's face. Centred in the door frame, he clapped his hands together.

"Guess what? A baby boy!"

Angela screamed with delight and all thoughts of yucky cereal were forgotten. I skipped down the road holding Dad's hand, demanding to be brought to the hospital immediately to see the new addition to our family. But, horror of horrors, it was a Sunday and I was told we had to go to Mass first to thank God for my new baby brother. My mind reeled.

"But I haven't seen my baby brother," I argued. "How can I thank God for my baby brother when I don't even know if I *have* a baby brother because I haven't *seen* my baby brother?" Dad managed to ignore the increasingly high-pitched desperation in my voice and somehow my logic escaped him. I don't think I had ever caveated a prayer before but I made sure to point out to God that my thanks was all based on hearsay – that I had yet to have sight of the new brother I was thanking him for. (Oh yes, I was a lawyer in the making at that stage.)

Of course, now I realise that Dad was giving my poor mum a few hours' rest after being up all night giving birth to an eight-pound six-ounce lump. As soon as Mass was over, Dad's own desire to get back to his son got the better of him and we arrived at the maternity ward, grinning like a pair of idiots. To this day, I love the smell of hospitals. Most people hate it because they associate those places with sickness, and sometimes even death. For me, my first experience of a hospital was one of unrivalled happiness.

When I saw Mum, I forgot about the baby and ran to her, having not seen her since the day before. Then she pointed to him. I looked down and it was like life before him had never existed.

I think my parents were concerned I'd lose all my friends because whenever my little girl pals came over to the house I refused to play our usual games. There was only one thing I wanted to play: "Watch the Baby." As he was usually asleep, my friends didn't find it nearly as interesting as I did.

As he got older, my brother and I made up our own games, such as "The Teacher and the Boy". I recall it involved me playing a teacher, while he starred as a boy. Not particularly imaginative but that didn't stop us. He was my "I Spy" partner on long trips (pre-motorway) from Dublin to Galway. We were climbing-frame monkeys, snowmen makers, snakes-and-ladders competitors and sandcastle builders.

And he became the subject of my first ever publication. A poem, in the letters pages of the girls' comic, *Bunty*. It was entitled "My Baby Brother" and began: "*I have a baby brother, I wouldn't want another.*" The general comment about this line was: "You're so right, little brothers can be annoying!" Which is true. There was the time we tried to complete a giant maze together. He abandoned me and was out in three minutes; almost an hour later I was still stuck in there and the manager of the fairground had to come in to get me. And there was the time when it transpired that "going for a swim" meant him cannonballing me until I had to get out of the pool.

But he had his uses. Who else but a little brother can you make do anything, just by telling him you'll time him? And that weekend we stayed on my great-uncle's boat and one of us had to sleep on the floor: all I had to do was pretend I wanted the floor instead of the couch and he kicked up a fuss, demanding whatever I wanted. Comfy night on the couch for me! He provided hours of amusement – I particularly like the one where Dad caught him on the phone to the Gardaí reporting my parents for making him eat his vegetables.

He's all grown up now. It's been strange, watching him morph into a man. There are seven years between us – the kid basically had three parents growing up. But now he's an adult it's different. We're friends.

My brother was such an important part of my childhood that it's hard to reminisce without mentioning him. But there is another reason he comes to mind as I write this piece. Within three weeks of my daydreaming paying off and my book being published, my brother's own dream came true. He is jetting off to America, for at least one year. He loves the States. It is a big and colourful place, brimming with opportunities. He'll do great there.

So if I could go back, what would I say to that young girl who sat for hours at "Billy's Table" in our living room (we called it that because my *Billy in the Barrel* toy used to sit at the corner of it) writing her stories and playing "Watch the Baby" while he slept in?

I'd say that with your novel finally making it, and your brother leaving for the foreseeable future, you're going to end up admitting the truth about those first lines of your first ever published poem. "*I have a baby brother, I wouldn't want another.*" It was assumed I meant that I wouldn't want a second brother, because they are such pains. Everyone seemed to find it amusing, so I never corrected them. But that isn't what I meant.

Can you not guess from my "I love everybody" and "Nice

Nine" stories? I meant that I loved my baby brother so much I wouldn't exchange him for any other boy. I wouldn't want another child to be my sibling because I already had the best one going.

So, young Jennifer, my advice is keep doing what you're doing – keep playing with your little brother. Make the most of him while he's little because he has big dreams and won't be your baby forever (also he eventually gets a decent growing spurt and takes pleasure in standing beside you, looking down and smirking).

Oh, and keep daydreaming. It'll make a writer of you one day!

Jennifer Burke is a Dublin-based author and solicitor. After winning the 'Write a Bestseller' competition run by Poolbeg Press and TV3, her first novel, *The Secret Son*, was published in September 2013. She is an active member of the Irish Writers' Centre where she regularly attends events and takes part in a monthly novel-writing group. She also writes shorter fiction. Having been shortlisted in the 2012 Cork County Council 'From the Well' competition, she had her short story published in the resulting anthology. She was also shortlisted in the 'Fish Publishing Flash Fiction' competition in both 2012 and 2013.

The Perfect Day

Colette Caddle

I would wake up, at thirteen, in my very own bedroom. I was about sixteen before I had a room to myself. I think it's only if you've shared that you really understand the luxury of having your own space, especially as a teenager. My room would not be pink and fluffy with wall-to-wall cuddly toys but probably quite plain and white with an enormous bookshelf crammed with all my favourite, dog-eared reads. My MP3 player – if I'm going back in time then I'm taking technology with me – would be in its dock complete with the best speakers and belting out Michael Bublé's "The Best is Yet to Come" – hey, it's a good song, he's hot and I am only thirteen!

My "actual" MP3 at the time was one of the most treasured possessions of my youth: a radio. It was a small but bulky contraption but that didn't stop me shoving it under my pillow and listening to radio Luxembourg. It didn't have anything as sophisticated as a "sleep" button so, if my dad didn't spot and remove it when he was tucking me in, I was liable to knock against the volume key in the middle of the night and blast my ear off or it would play all night long. I went through a lot of batteries.

I would start my day with a shower. A *real* shower, not those dismal yokes we used to have that hung over the bath and you had to run around underneath to get wet. And the temperature would neither leave me with first-degree burns nor give me frostbite; it would be a Goldilocks special – just right.

I would be a cool kid and so I would dress cool . . . cheesecloth shirt, Levi straight jeans and clogs or desert boots – youngsters among you, just think Uggs. My hair would not be the untameable bush that caused me so much heartache in my teens but instead would have miraculously morphed into a mane of shining silken waves that would fall in a perfect curtain around my shoulders.

Naturally it would be a beautiful, summer day with an indigo-blue sky and just the occasional puffy white cloud and the sun would neither burn me nor add more freckles. After a breakfast of corn flakes and buttery toast I would head off, full of excitement, to summer camp.

You see, we didn't have summer camps back in the seventies. We played against the wall with a tennis racquet and ball or churned up the garden to create an impromptu golf course or cricket pitch. We set up the family tent and pretended we were camping – I'm not sure why we had that tent – we never actually *went* camping. Not that I'm complaining. Damp ground, creepy-crawlies, scary noises and Irish weather guaranteed that it was never going to make my top-ten list of perfect holidays. On days when we felt really inventive we built a den or a go-kart – we called them trolleys – from any old planks, nails and discarded household objects that we found in our garage or shed. It was all good fun despite the bruises and skinned knees, but we were kids so of course we got bored from time to time.

But I'm not sure that I would enjoy the standard summer-camp format. There's too much sport and I've never been the sporty sort. But the camps that specialise in one activity would be a different matter entirely.

When I'm checking out things for my sons to do in the long summer months I am mesmerised at the range of camps on offer and a tad jealous. So, if I could beam myself back to my fourteenth summer, it would be to go to summer camp. As this is fantasy fiction, the best ones with the best teachers would obviously be in my neighbourhood . . . work with me here, it's make-believe.

First my day would last longer than normal earth days. I'm not sure if I'm going with the *Doctor Who* or *Hitchhiker's Guide* philosophy but basically a mediocre detail like time would not be an issue. So exactly what activities would I go for? First up, I would attend some sort of theatre summer camp. No, I do not mean one that attracts *X-Factor* hopefuls, involves ringlets, tap shoes or fake tan, but a serious one for kids who want to learn the craft, not become famous overnight. I'd like to go to one with a choreographer that would teach intricate dance routines which, naturally, I would pick up very quickly. The camp would have a vocal coach who would teach breathing techniques and send me home sounding like a mini Imelda May and of course I would be schooled in the serious business of acting. Now, I'm inclined to think that actors are born not made, but for the purpose of this story I would be the exception.

With that under my belt an art summer camp would be next on my list. Now please don't confuse art with arts and crafts. I have a horror of all things crafty. All that glue, glitter, pastes and pottery is the stuff of nightmares and messy, sticky ones at that. I have no burning ambition to make a volcano – no pun intended – or a lopsided mug or a lumpy garish cushion with *Best Mum* on it. I'd simply like to learn more about drawing and painting, thank you very much.

I loved art as a kid but when I chose to study the subject for my Junior Certificate it stopped being fun. I can't say it was the teacher's fault – I barely remember her – and I do know that a couple of my fellow students went on to make art their profession. Perhaps I was just put off by the fact that now it was work rather than play and, instead of spending the entire time with a brush in my hand, I was expected to study the history of art and learn the "rules".

But there are no rules in art . . . are there? Just look at Tracey Emin or Andy Warhol. Everyone knows now that the teachers who chastised children for not colouring within the lines got it completely wrong, putting limits on young imaginations and stunting creativity. So on my dream day my teacher would be innovative, nurturing, and fun, and I would trip happily off to camp full of confidence. It goes without saying that I would return home at the end of the day with at least one masterpiece.

I actually took up painting again a couple of years ago when I was having trouble with a storyline and I needed something to calm and distract me for a few hours. I got such pleasure from experimenting with colours and textures and I found it very liberating to do something that was for my pleasure alone. It was okay to go a little bit crazy – and I did! I was like the proverbial kid in a sweetshop as I abandoned paintbrushes and used anything that came to mind to create the effect that I was trying to achieve. I messed about with plastic cutlery, a sponge and even a cocktail stick – absolutely marvellous for authentic-looking blades of grass. But I have to admit that I got the most fun of all from using my fingers to create a thunderous sky or a stormy sea. I know, I know, I'm such a rebel.

I also think I'd have enjoyed a cookery camp. I did get lessons in school but they were more practical than inspiring and my rock buns were aptly named. Cooking wasn't cool in the seventies and most of the TV programmes were serious productions with basic, sensible recipes and rather boring. The highlight was Keith Floyd getting tipsy and shouting at his producer. I rarely cooked at home as my mother was a brilliant cook and excelled at baking so why mess with perfection? But, once I started to eat more and got to try different cuisines, I began to experiment. Just like art I found it quite relaxing and therapeutic and to my knowledge I haven't poisoned anyone yet. Just imagine what I could do after lessons from a top chef! I think someone like Jean Christophe Novelli would fit the bill. He would not only nurture my love for cooking but be the perfect heartthrob for the teenage Colette to moon over.

There's another summer camp that I'd like to attend on my perfect day . . . I'm sure you can guess. Yes, creative writing.

English was always my favourite subject and any new schoolbooks were read long before the beginning of term in September. I enjoyed writing essays and I actually won a prize from the National Dairy Council for my essay on the story of milk. In hindsight, though, my success may have been because I wrote it from the cow's viewpoint and included a racy paragraph about a bull rather than the quality of my prose.

But, seriously, it never occurred to me that writing could be anything other than an enjoyable hobby. The dear little nun who took care of career guidance had a very simple way of looking at things. If you were brainy you went to university to study to be a doctor, a dentist, a lawyer or a teacher. If you were good with your hands, then you were encouraged to learn a trade. And the rest of us were told to take a typing/secretarial course and/or apply for jobs in the banks, building societies, insurance companies and the civil service. I did as I was told, it never occurred to me to do otherwise, and I was very anxious to have a monthly pay cheque and independence and so I ended up in an insurance company.

Had there been a different attitude to writing and other creative talents would my life have turned out differently? Maybe not and perhaps it's better that way. There is no doubt that the more of life you experience, the more you have to write about. But would I have enjoyed a summer course that was about writing, not for homework or an exam, but just for the pure love of it? Damn right I would. And so, on my special day, I would attend a course given by a brilliant teacher who would fan the flames of that love and make the possibility of writing as a career not so far-fetched after all.

Under the guidance of my mentor I would write an innovative and exciting story that would amaze and enchant, and as the teacher would know an editor in a successful publishing company, within a matter of weeks word of my amazing book deal and six-figure advance would hit the headlines and I would be an overnight sensation. Live with it . . . this is *my* fantasy, remember?

I should point out that between my various activities on My

Day I would only be eating foods that I liked. Friends would not pull faces at my tomato or banana sandwiches or make fun of my love for bread and brown sauce, and dinner that evening would be a runny fried egg and chips complete with bread and butter to make the perfect buttie.

Now to round off my day what would I do? I suppose again I would want to do something that was unheard of when I actually *was* thirteen: go to a concert. Yes, I had been to shows and pantomimes with my family but not to a live gig with a real-life pop star. My first concert was Kid Creole and the Coconuts – I was about seventeen – and my second, a year later, was Bryan Ferry. The only reason I was allowed go to either was because I was with my big brother. So if I could have gone to see anyone at all at thirteen, who would it have been?

Ah, now this is the part of the story where I may live to regret my honesty. I had quite eclectic tastes – still do. But as the youngest of a family of five I was naturally influenced – after reading you may say tainted – by the tastes of my siblings. To say they were wide-ranging is an understatement. Step forward, Leonard Cohen and Neil Young, who I'm proud to say I still enjoy today. There was a little of Elvis, a lot of Neil Diamond – I went to see him quite recently and, laugh if you must, but I thought he was great! I also liked a lot of show tunes and musicals from *My Fair Lady* to *Jesus Christ Superstar*. Add to the mix some Horslips, Planxty, Thin Lizzy and Genesis and throw in a dash of angst via Janis Ian, Joan Armatrading and Carole King. And I make no apology whatsoever for playing James Taylor's "You've Got a Friend", Cat Stevens' "Father and Son" and Jim Croce's "Time in a Bottle" over and over again. Deep breath. Yes, it's true. I also liked The Carpenters, Bread, Neil Sedaka and Barry Manilow. I loved David Essex – okay, it was his eyes and smile rather than his voice and, gulp, I had the most enormous crush on David Soul . . . I am never going to live this down, am I? But we all have our musical skeletons. At least a Bay City Roller record (that's CD, youngsters) never entered my house and I didn't fancy Gary Glitter . . . perish the thought, shudder.

But one icon that I loved then and still admire today gets to play Dublin in my fantasy concert and that's David Bowie. I imagine his *Ziggy Stardust* would have been a night that I wouldn't forget in a hurry. As Ireland's newest VIP I would be in the front row and when David saw me mouth every word to every song he would draw me up on stage, look into my eyes and sing to me. I would be invited to the party backstage afterwards where on discovery that I was Ireland's latest and greatest author he would beg to read my book and then introduce me to one of his best friends who just happened to be a movie director.

The book would become a bestseller and the film would go on to be a blockbuster with David and me obviously playing the lead roles and after I was nominated for an Oscar – oh, you're leaving? Okay then. Turn the light off on your way out, would you? And keep the noise down, I'm quite enjoying this dream.

Colette Caddle writes contemporary women's fiction. She was first published by Poolbeg Press in 1999 and as a result of her first book, *Too Little Too Late*, holding the number one spot in Ireland for three weeks, she became the subject of a bidding war among eight UK publishers. She is now published by Simon & Schuster and has written thirteen books, which are available in Ireland, the US, the UK and commonwealth countries, and have been translated into seven languages. Her books are also available in e-format through Amazon. Her next book, *First We Take Manhattan*, will be published in Ireland in January 2014 and go on general release in August. She is married with two sons and lives in north County Dublin. You can contact Colette through her website colettecaddle.com, find her on Facebook at Colette Caddle Books or follow her on Twitter: @colettecaddle.

Rocks for Sale

Janet E Cameron

I'm the oldest in a family of three girls. When I look back, I remember a lot of good times: noise, energy, rushing up and down the stairs, one idea after another that would end up transforming the whole house. We'd decide we were going to build a tree house or put on a play in the garage, turn the backyard into a race track. Or we'd make up long rewrites of fairy tales and act them out into a tape recorder – usually these just involved the princes and princesses belching at each other. The house was full of clutter and chaos, cats, dogs and guinea pigs, junk from everyone's hobby of the moment.

It was probably inevitable that we'd get in each other's way – and we did, almost every second we were together. Insults and arguments. Elbows knocking against elbows at the dinner table. Car rides that were sites for hours of psychological warfare.

"Dad, Judy's looking at me! She's breathing on me!"

My dad would shake his head wearily from the driver's seat. "Girls, stop looking. Stop breathing."

My sister Judy was a year and a half younger than me, and the smartest person I knew, though back then I never would have admitted this. Fighting with her seemed like a matter of survival.

Neither of us could let the smallest thing go. I remember telling her I never learned to whistle. But it was no big deal, I went on defensively, lots of people couldn't. Judy was on the phone in seconds going through a list of all her friends.

"That's why you called me?" I heard one girl say. "You want me to *whistle*?"

"Just do it!" Judy told her, looking over the breakfast table at me in triumph.

My relationship with Fiona was a bit different. Judy and I were too close in almost every way. But Fiona was five years younger, sweet and agreeable, and she'd believe whatever Judy and I decided to tell her. "We're going to play hide-and-seek," we might say, and then go off and watch TV while she waited all afternoon in some dark corner of the attic for us to come and find her. Or there was the time Fiona got a splinter in her thumb and asked Judy what it was. "This means," my sister informed her gravely, "you have two weeks left to live." Fiona marched into my room and demanded to know if it was true, and I remember Judy was mad at me for days because I wouldn't back her up.

We lived in a quiet little town in the countryside, idyllic for childhood, boring as a daylong detention for teenagers. There were wide streets lined with shady trees and tall wooden houses – I'd spend days running around exploring every corner. In the summer my feet were usually covered in grit and bits of dried lawn. I never bothered with shoes much.

It was a Saturday morning in late June – I was almost twelve and Judy and Fiona would have been ten and seven – when Judy burst into the kitchen as I was looking for cereal. The screen door yawned and slammed shut behind her.

"You won't believe what Fiona's doing! Get out there!" Judy was overjoyed, glowing – the way she always looked when one of us had made a complete fool of herself.

So I went outside. The sun was casting jigsaw patterns of light and dark over the front yard. Somewhere a lawnmower growled and thrummed to itself. Where was Fiona? And what was she doing to make Judy so happy?

Then I saw my sister. She was standing behind a low concrete wall that separated the driveway from the back yard, wearing her summer uniform of a swimsuit with shorts over it, knee socks and red sneakers. Every few seconds she'd flip her hair out of her eyes – she had long bangs and they grew fast. The top of the concrete wall was strewn with a collection of rocks and pebbles.

I couldn't figure this out. Finally I asked my sister what she was doing out there.

"It's my store. I'm having a rock sale."

This was too good. "Rocks? Who do you think is going to buy this stuff?"

She didn't answer. Instead she stared grimly ahead, her jaw tense and her chin dimpling. The expression of someone trying to tune out a taunting bully. I was instantly ashamed of myself, then angry at her for making me feel this way. I slammed back into the house.

Judy and I sat at the breakfast table, laughing at our little sister. By then our parents had joined us in the kitchen – just out of bed and trying to navigate the day. Dad was still in pyjamas, his hair a wild nest abandoned by seabirds. The eggs in the frying pan bubbled and snapped at him. Mom was in her nightgown and turquoise terrycloth bathrobe, wrestling cereal bowls into the clawed rack of the dishwasher.

"You kids stop it," she said. "I think it's nice your sister's trying to do something different."

We started talking over each other. It was a dopey idea, we insisted. Fiona would be out there all day embarrassing us, and no one could even see that back wall from the street anyway.

"You're just jealous," she said.

Judy said she was going to compete and have a dirt sale, or maybe a used toilet-paper sale. Mom told us again to stop it. Dad slid an oily egg onto a plate with a dark round of toast and banged it on the table in front of us.

"That's enough," he said. He left the room, and we could hear the stairs creaking.

Judy and I looked at each other.

"It's not fair," she said to Mom. "You guys always take her side." But she didn't have her usual conviction.

Dad shuffled back into the kitchen and stood over us for a moment. Then he leaned down, took my wrist and pressed a handful of change into my palm.

"Go and buy some rocks from your sister."

"But Dad! It's stupid!"

"Do it anyway."

I looked at the coins in my hand. "Can I keep some of this?"

"No."

Okay, fine. I had to buy rocks from Fiona.

I watched her from the kitchen window. An elderly couple strolled past. "Rocks for sale!" she called, in her thin little voice. They smiled at her but didn't stop. It's possible they couldn't hear much of anything from the sidewalk.

I couldn't face Fiona yet. I wasn't sure why. Instead I skulked into the living room and plopped myself in front of the Atari game console, which we'd connected to an old black-and-white TV I'd dragged home from a yard sale. I spent a few vacant minutes shooting at blocky grey aliens descending apathetically towards my spaceship, in no particular hurry to destroy the earth. Dad and Judy were in the kitchen arguing. After a while I switched off the machine and slouched out the front door to go check out this sale.

But Fiona wasn't at her post. The rocks were just sitting there. Had she given up? Was it my fault? I stood drilled into place by the morning sun, my shadow falling across the top of the wall. Our neighbour came out of her front door loaded down with gardening equipment and a tray full of purple snapdragons.

"Is that your rock sale?" she called out.

"No!"

I looked closer. Actually, these were pretty good rocks. It looked like she'd gathered them on the beach over the mountain. Some were smooth and egg-shaped, others had stripes fusing two colours together. There were a few craggy ones with tiny snowflakes of quartz pressed into them. I wouldn't mind setting these on my windowsill.

I decided on my own price range, chose six or seven I liked, and left piles of quarters and dimes in their place, all the money Dad had given me. We lived in the kind of town where you could do this – leave money on a wall all afternoon. The sun reflected off the little shining circles as I walked away. I took the rocks upstairs to my room and got comfortable with an *Asterix* book.

After a while I heard a commotion in the kitchen, the screen door banging open and shut, Fiona shouting for Mom and Dad. My room was right above them and I could hear everything. Was she angry? Maybe I hadn't left enough change. Or it could be she'd wanted to save the rocks for real customers.

"Mom! Dad!" Fiona said. "While I was in the bathroom *all these people* came to the rock sale! Come and look!"

I angled myself at my window until I could make out the scene below, Fiona showing our parents the small piles of change where her rocks had been. She took her place behind the wall again with what seemed like a renewed sense of purpose, looking forward to another rush of customers. I hid the rocks in the top drawer of my bedside table.

I was just sliding the drawer shut when Judy arrived. She flopped down on the bed and started flipping through my *Asterix* book.

"Why do you like this stuff? All they do is punch each other." She put the book down and it bumped onto the floor. "And can you believe anybody came to that sale? I bet it was just Mom and Dad."

"It totally wasn't. It was me."

She refused to believe it. I opened the drawer and showed her the rocks.

"Cool." She sprang up. "I'm gonna go tell her."

"No, stop!"

Judy was out of my room and down the hall in seconds. I chased after my sister, picturing Fiona's face as she realised her mystery customers were just me, that her sale wasn't the town-wide success she'd thought it had been. Judy was receding into the distance. I could hear her giggling away as I thundered down the stairs. She lost me on the way to the kitchen – she'd pulled her favourite trick of opening and closing one door to make you think she'd gone through it and then sprinting off in another direction. Never failed.

By the time I got outside it was too late. She was at Fiona's shop counter. What were they saying to each other? If I ran, I could smack a hand over her mouth and drag her away. But that might look kind of obvious. Fiona would demand to know what was going on, and then we'd both have to tell her.

So I stayed on the porch, waiting for the yelling, the tears, for Fiona to stomp off and leave her rocks sitting forlorn and abandoned on their concrete wall. But wait. My sisters seemed to be chatting, almost pleasantly. Judy turned and left the store and Fiona was smiling after her.

"Nah, I didn't bother telling," Judy said later. "Let her think what she wants. It's funnier that way." But I noticed her pockets were bulging with all the rocks she'd bought.

Had she really been planning on telling Fiona anything? Or did she just feel like driving me crazy? With Judy, you could never be sure.

That night I heard Fiona counting up the day's tally. "Mom bought rocks. And Judy. And Mrs Hinxman. And . . . and . . . all those people!"

Dad told me I'd done well. It felt better than winning an argument, better than being right.

The rocks stayed in the top drawer of my bedside table for years – with my secrets and contraband, diaries and letters, a pack of cigarettes I'd stolen from Dad. Long past the time Fiona would have recognised them. When I finally told her what had happened we were both in our twenties.

"I just thought there were a lot of people in the neighbourhood who wanted to buy rocks." She was laughing. "That was nice of you, Jan."

I wish I'd been nice more often. I didn't know how quickly

that childhood time would pass, or how much I'd miss my sisters when I left home. We spent so much of our time together fighting and competing. Such a waste. There should have been more moments like that – the day I decided to keep the secret of the rock sale. If I could be a child again, I hope I'd remember this.

Janet E Cameron is a Canadian writer and teacher living in Ireland. She grew up in a small town in Nova Scotia and since then has lived in Halifax, Toronto, Montreal, Vancouver, Tokyo, and Dublin. In 2012 she graduated with distinction from Trinity College Dublin with a Master's in Philosophy in Creative Writing. Her thesis was an excerpt from a novel which became *Cinnamon Toast and the End of the World*, the story of a restless kid growing up in rural Nova Scotia in the late 1980s, whose world comes to an end when he discovers that he's in love with his best friend Mark. *Cinnamon Toast* was one of the winners at the Irish Writers' Centre's inaugural Novel Fair in 2012, and was published to critical acclaim in Ireland and Canada by Hachette in early 2013. Janet is currently teaching at Dublin Business School and working on a second novel.

Miss Angel and Other
Bad Influences

Anna Carey

I have always been the sort of person who would read the back of a shampoo bottle rather than be left alone with my own thoughts for more than two minutes, so it's not surprising that I read an awful lot as a child. I devoured the works of everyone from E Nesbit to Judy Blume, from Richmal Crompton to Roald Dahl, but I also had an appetite for less literary fare. Every single Wednesday throughout my childhood, my dad would bring home the latest comics to me and my three sisters. Each of us started out at a very early age with *Twinkle*, before moving on to the *Beano* and, most significantly, *Mandy*, *Judy* and *Bunty*.

Girls' comics were a big part of my childhood. Not only did we get all three of the aforementioned comics every week, as well as the odd issue of *Tammy* or *Tracy*, but my grandparents ran a newsagent's shop in Kells, and when I was about ten we found a large stack of consecutive old issues of *Mandy* and *Judy* in the shop's storeroom. Reading our way through the piles became a high point of our Kells visits, until the dark day when we arrived to discover that our much-younger cousins had ripped them all up (I'm still a bit annoyed about that). But what exactly were we reading about?

49

When people reminisce about girls' comics, they tend to mention the likes of the Four Marys – good-natured romps about intrepid boarding-school girls. What they fail to mention is that the relatively ordinary Marys were not entirely typical of the medium. In fact, many, if not most, of the stories in girls' comics were either completely insane, completely terrifying, completely messed up, or all three. This is a medium in which a story about a girl who flies around the universe in a sentient space ship which is also a large rabbit is completely normal (the story was called "The Flights of Flopear", by the way). It's also a medium in which the vast majority of stories involved terrible things happening to relatively innocent girls.

Orphans were particularly popular in girls' comics. In fact, looking back, it feels like hardly any of the subjects lived with their biological parents. While some of the orphans lived in the present day (like Bella the gymnast, a beloved *Tammy* character who lived with her scheming aunt and uncle), comics readers generally preferred their orphans to be Victorian. And no one gathered together Victorian orphans like Miss Angel from *Mandy*. Angela Hamilton was a rich young lady in Victorian London who discovered she was dying of an unspecified but vaguely tubercular illness so, in order to spare her parents the pain of watching her die slowly, decided to fake her own death and go off and run a sort of orphanage in a stable, which became known as the Stable House, where the waifs called her Miss Angel.

No, the whole death-faking thing didn't make much sense. In fact, even as a small child, I could see the many faults in Angel's plan. If she was going to die anyway, surely it was better to let her parents spend as much time with her as possible? Also, and more crucially, if Angel had stayed in her giant comfortable mansion with her incredibly rich parents, she could have used the family's money to run a proper children's home with decent facilities rather than scrabbling around looking for pennies to keep her "waifs" in a manky old stable.

But logic was never the strong point of girls'-comic

melodramas. And so every week we would read how Miss Angel encountered yet another orphan (or two, if the first orphan had a sibling) with a picturesque back story and took them into the Stable House. Angel's adventures were so popular that she popped up in *Mandy* every few years, her stories usually introduced by a modern-day character who discovered Angel's diary and became entranced by her, much like the comic's readers themselves. In fact, we couldn't get enough Victorian misery. After reading the *Bunty* story "Workhouse Wendy" (in which a rich young girl goes undercover in the workhouse owned by her parents while they go on holiday and ends up stuck there when they're lost at sea), my sister Jenny and I went through a phase of drinking soup and pretending it was gruel.

Of course, as few ten-year-old girls were going to fake their own deaths and then run secret stable-based orphanages, or go undercover in a workhouse, there was little danger of readers being influenced by Miss Angel and Wendy. Some of the other stories, however, gave out more worrying messages. Countless comics stories involved characters being bullied or manipulated in some way, by classmates or siblings or wicked aunts or step-parents. Many of these stories involved characters being unfairly blamed for something they hadn't done, which was particularly painful to read.

Perhaps the greatest of these stories was "The Honourable S.J." which appeared in *Judy*. The eponymous S.J. was a girl with the brilliantly Dickensian name of Sarah-Jane Cheetwell. Her main victim was a girl called Ann, whose father worked for S.J.'s father. When Ann arrived as a scholarship girl at the boarding school where the sneaky, constantly sneering S.J. was inexplicably head girl, S.J. began blackmailing her to do her bidding, saying that Ann's father would lose his job if his daughter defied the all-powerful S.J..

S.J., however, proved such a popular villain that even though she was expelled from the school after her first adventure, she had to return to the pages of *Judy*. What baffled me as a child was that, despite having been expelled for blackmail and bullying, S.J. would inevitably end up in a position of authority at the next school she attended. Didn't anyone ask why she'd left her previous school? How come she would always be made head girl or at least prefect as soon as she arrived at a new place? Anyway, S.J. always found a few more victims to torment but she and Ann kept bumping into each other, even when they both ended up at an Alpine finishing school. I like to think that if the comics had continued, they'd have been facing each other across a boardroom somewhere.

Ann may have been blackmailed, but most of the bullying victims in comics simply chose not to speak out. "What's the point?" they'd say. "Nobody will ever believe me!" Sometimes they would decide that their parents or siblings would just be too upset if they knew how bad the bullying was. In the comics world, the only way your bully would get her comeuppance would be if other people overheard her making a terrible threat, ideally over a microphone that the bully foolishly believed had been switched off. That was the thing about girls' comics – their characters simply had to suffer, even if – especially if – the suffering was avoidable.

In fact, one of the most unsettling trends in girls' comics was the sheer amount of stories in which the heroine suffers horribly but voluntarily, supposedly to help others. The most ludicrously dreadful example of this was "Hard Hearted Harriet", in which the eponymous orphan heroine discovered she was dying and so tried to make her younger siblings hate her, so that they wouldn't mind so much when she eventually died. The thought that maybe it might be more traumatic in the long run for the kids to be cruelly rejected by their beloved sister didn't seem to cross her mind. Comics were full of stories in which girls masochistically made themselves into hate figures, supposedly for the greater good. It was as if the readers, and the writers, couldn't get enough of pointless suffering.

Of course, at least the sufferings of Harriet et al weren't of the supernatural variety. I still maintain that the "spooky" stories in girls' comics are the most deeply disturbing things I've ever read.

Some of the supernatural stories were harmless – like "Valda, Girl of Mystery" from *Mandy*. Valda was always turning up in jungles or snowy mountain ranges wearing nothing but a green minidress. She was basically immortal as long as she kept her energy topped up with her magic crystal (*"The crystal of life is death to all but me!"* she'd cry whenever anyone tried to steal it, and she was right).

But most of the supernatural stories were completely terrifying. Basically, they would involve a girl being punished for some minor character flaw (being a bit lazy or selfish) by being turned into a hideous creature or trapped forever in a painting or a paperweight or something. In one story, a girl who is always late, to the annoyance of her friends, is late for a Halloween party. She thinks she's joining her friends when she gets on the train filled with people in scary masks. But they just stare at her, and the story ends with the train going into a tunnel as the terrified girl says, *"You are my friends, aren't you? Aren't you?"*

And that's the last anyone will ever see of her, because in the world of comics being stuck on a terrifying ghost train for all eternity is a suitable punishment for a lack of punctuality. In an even more unsettling story, "I Am Margaret", a girl who is rude to an old gypsy woman wakes up the next day with her face and voice grotesquely transformed. *"But I am Margaret!"* she wails in the final hideous panel. This was all the stuff of nightmares.

Sometimes the victims of the horror were completely innocent. When I was about nine, I was so genuinely terrified by a deeply disturbing story in a *Diana* annual about evil garden gnomes who come to life and consume an entire family that I threw the annual in the bin, and then couldn't relax until bin day arrived and the offending annual was taken away to the dump. Less horrifying but still creepy was "Little Stranger", a masterpiece of paranoia in a which an only child wakes up to discover she's suddenly got a younger sister whom everyone claims has always been there but is revealed to be an evil mind-controlling alien.

So what did the several generations of Irish and British girls who grew up on these comics learn from our weekly dose of feverish melodrama? You could argue that we learned that being a girl meant suffering stoically, and sacrificing your own wellbeing for the sake of others; that we had to be perfect and that if we were selfish or lazy we'd be punished hideously; that if we were being badly treated there was no point in speaking out because no one would believe us anyway. These were messages that reinforced the idea of women as victims or selfless Stepford Wives and, as a feminist, I look back at them in horror.

And yet, despite all these terrifying messages, I can't help feeling a bit sad that those comics are all gone now. They provided me with a huge amount of entertainment throughout my childhood. And, maybe because I was lucky enough to grow up in a happy, secure home with good friends, I was able to see how crazy the values of the characters often were. In fact, laughing at Miss Angel's ludicrous saintliness was part of the fun.

But perhaps the reason I was so fond of these comics is that they presented a vision of the world in which girls were important. Sure, they suffered. But they were also often brave and determined and creative, and they were always the focus of the story. In a world where female characters are still sidelined (a study showed that in the one hundred highest-grossing movies at the US box office in 2012, only 28.4% of speaking characters were female, and I can't imagine things were better when I was a child in the 1980s), *Mandy*, *Judy*, *Bunty* and their ilk showed that girls could be the centre of the fictional universe. Even if that universe was a little bit warped.

Anna Carey is a journalist and author. She grew up in Drumcondra in Dublin and studied German and History of Art at Trinity College Dublin before taking an MA in Journalism at Dublin City University. Her first young adult novel, *The Real Rebecca*, won the Senior Children's Book prize at the 2011 Irish Book

Awards, and the sequel, *Rebecca's Rules*, was shortlisted for the same prize in 2012. Her third book, *Rebecca Rocks*, was published this year. She's a regular contributor to the *Irish Times* and RTÉ, and the co-founder of the feminist website and podcast the Anti Room. She likes feminism, singing, confident small dogs and books written and set during the 1930s and 1940s. She lives in north Dublin with her husband Patrick Freyne in a small house full of books and music. She still loves comics.

The Generals

Ann Carroll

Sister Cronin's strengths were planning and execution and she could have been a great general. But sixty years ago an army career wasn't an option, so instead of soldiers she had fifty-six small girls at her command. Her base was the national school in Larkhill, Whitehall, Dublin and her campaign was the First Holy Communion, 1953.

Every morning during the weeks beforehand, she paced over and back at the head of the class. Our eyes swivelled with her.

"We need precise preparation, children. What do we need?"

"Precise preparation, Sister!" we bawled enthusiastically. A lack of enthusiasm could earn us a stint in the corner.

"And what does precise preparation mean, girls?"

"Attention to detail, Sister!" we roared.

No one let their mind wander during this warm-up routine, not after one unfortunate had nodded off and been threatened with no Holy Communion at all. This had caused terrible shock. No Holy Communion surely wasn't possible? No lovely dresses . . . no special day . . . no presents of money . . . How would we tell our mammies?

So we were Sister Cronin's willing troops.

The opening part of her campaign was our First Confession, for which we learned our Catechism: *Do unto others as you would that they should do unto you. Do good to them that hate you and pray for them that persecute and calumniate you.*

'Them' doesn't seem like good grammar but that's how we learned it. And though the gist was beyond us, the sounds were great.

Then we learned the Ten Commandments, nearly all of which were incomprehensible.

"There's no need to understand them. Sure you can't commit most of the sins mentioned in them!" Sister Cronin told us.

This gave them a wonderful promise of mystery and future wickedness.

We were to examine our consciences, she said, by sticking to the ones about honouring our father and mother and not stealing.

"Are you sure the priest can't tell anyone our sins, Sister?" I asked, worried he might broadcast the fact that I'd robbed Frances Kelly's new multicoloured pencil. Frances was inclined to be aggressive and if she found out, I'd be bashed up.

"How many times must I tell you?" Sister Cronin said. "What you say in the confessional is confidential!"

"Does that mean he can't tell anyone?" I always liked things clear.

"He can tell *no one*. What have you done anyway? Is it murder?"

Eager to hide the truth, I said, "No, Sister, but I might have calumniated." Someone must have distracted her for I don't remember the rest of that conversation.

Then Sister Cronin taught us the Act of Contrition. A great morning was spent getting each child to kneel down as she would in the confession box, bless herself and say this prayer. After fifty-six rehearsals there wasn't one who didn't know it for life.

When Sister explained the True Purpose of Amendment I secretly left a pencil on Frances Kelly's desk. It was a bit small and chewed but I'd lost the original.

On the day of our First Confession we were marched two by two from the school up to the little wooden church. We were warned to keep our heads bowed, not to talk to any neighbours, not to pick flowers and not to pay any heed to the man selling sweets from his cart. We were especially to pay no heed to his horse. This was a pity as the horse was a favourite of mine, being able to move his teeth around the way my granny could. But no, we were to think only of our sins and have them off by heart for the priest.

The morning was a great success and we each emerged from the confession box, hands joined in prayer as we'd been taught, looking holy and self-conscious. The priest congratulated Sister Cronin on an excellent job.

She was in great form. "First battle over, children. Now we can prepare for your perfect day, the day of your First Holy Communion."

And so we practised kneeling again. Sister Cronin had a huge supply of unconsecrated hosts, which we learned to digest without chewing.

"Hold it in your mouth, child! Then swallow. This will be the Body of Christ. Do not munch!"

She told us about Transubstantiation. We'd no problem believing a wafer of bread and a goblet of wine turned into the Body and Blood of Christ. After all, at seven we were still young enough to believe that on one night of the year a big stout man dressed in red fitted down every child's chimney in the world, with his sack of presents. The sacrament of Communion was magical, and I couldn't wait for my soul, lodged somewhere near my heart, to become a shining white circle of goodness.

But before that could happen there was another general to please, this time on the home front where my mother was waging her own campaign to make this a special day.

"It'll be the best day of your life," she told me. "Perfect."

I was the youngest child, the only girl after six boys and my mother took great pride in making my clothes. But I didn't want a home-made frock for my Communion. Every other girl in the class was going to Clery's or MacBirneys and would be dressed to kill.

"What's Jennie Murphy wearing?" my mother asked one day. Jennie was my best friend.

"A dress from Clery's," I said. "But they're very well off," I added, already excusing what I'd be wearing.

"Huh. We're as good as them. Mrs Murphy is a romancer. We'll get everything in Arnott's so."

"Arnott's?" This was a cut above the rest.

"Sure why not? It's a day that will never happen again."

And so we went to town. My mother, who always counted the pennies, bought everything new: vest, knickers, petticoat, white socks and gloves as well as dress, veil, shoes and bag. And it was all top end. Then came the rosary beads, the white prayer book and precious Communion medal with its silver chain.

Now I was kitted out and I'd be brand new.

Afterwards, I realised how hard she must have saved for that day. There wasn't much money coming in. My father was a police sergeant and my eldest brother had just started in the Civil Service. Theirs were the only wages. The next two were twins, nineteen years old. One had emigrated to Canada and the other was in the Augustinian College in Rathfarnham, training to be a priest. The youngest three were at boarding school so money had to be found for fees, uniforms, books, sports-gear and footwear. Boys' shoes seemed to wear out at an alarming rate and my father tried to stop the process by nailing studs into the soles. This earned them the nicknames Horsy One, Two and Three as they clattered around their college.

I'd have thought my mother would find it painful to buy clothes that wouldn't be used for much more than one day, and that any old underwear would do since it wouldn't be seen. But her extravagance was wholehearted and I can remember her laying out every garment on the sofa in the sitting room – a room that was only used at Christmas or for visitors – and inviting my father to admire her purchases.

My father said it was all wonderful, and smiled and nodded,

very much the bit-player in our grand show.

The sun shone on cue the day I made my First Communion. We were up early, my mother and I, for Mass was at eight. I dressed and she took the rags out of my long hair and eased the sausage curls into shape. I fastened the crossover shoes. She slipped the silver chain and medal around my neck. Finally she placed the veil on my head and clipped it into place. Then we had a look in the long mirror.

"Perfect," she said.

I could only agree with her.

"This is the best day of your life," she said again.

She said it with such feeling that I remembered the words always. In later years I thought she must have been thinking of her own First Communion.

When she was nine, her mother died after a long illness and after that she spent some very unhappy years in a girls' home. She often mentioned her mother and missed her all of her life, so her First Communion Day must have been a precious memory.

I don't remember much about the church ceremony. Presumably it went well, for I can still see Sister Cronin beaming at us. I do remember devouring a fry for breakfast, my mother's huge cardigan wrapped around me to protect the dress.

Jennie called and we took off on a round of the neighbours, accompanied by my mother's command: "Do not on any account get that dress dirty!"

At every house the women admired us, twirled us around and gave us a half crown each. Except for Mrs Gumley who gave us only a shilling. We discussed this lapse on our way down the road.

"Why only a bob?" I said. "Mammy says she's a very nice woman."

"My mammy says the same," said Jennie.

She came up with the answer. "I know! It's because she's a Protestant. Sure why would she give us anything? A shilling is *very* good for a Protestant!"

When I counted the money at home that evening it came to

three pounds, thirteen shillings and sixpence. A lavish amount which my mother later made me put it in the post office for a rainy day. Over the years it dwindled so much in value that, by the time I had sole control, the sum wouldn't have purchased the spoke of a brolly and this gave me a very jaundiced view of saving which has lasted a lifetime.

My father took out the old Ford, cranked it up and drove us around to Granny and then to the aunties where I was plied with cakes and lemonade. These could not be refused and each time my mother made sure to take her vast cardigan out of her bag and wrap it around me so that nothing touched my dress.

Afterwards we went to visit my brother the trainee-priest. My mother's views on his vocation were well aired. She thought a priest's life was no life at all and was pleased when he left three years later, got a job, married and had a family.

But on this day my brother was a particularly grave young man who gave me a holy picture. It wasn't a present I thought much of. No doubt a little crassness had entered the day with the earlier cash. Still, I had my photo taken with him in the gardens at Orlagh and that's something still to treasure.

We were home again and it was after tea when I went around to visit Mrs Murphy, Jennie's mother. The best till last. She was a lovely woman, always welcoming.

She'd already seen my dress at the church but she wanted to make a bit of a fuss. I sat down with Jennie to a large slice of chocolate cake and some orange squash and without further ado knocked over the glass so the bright liquid poured down my front.

"Jesus! Your mammy!" Mrs Murphy shrieked. "What are we going to do?"

She made me take off the dress immediately and luckily the bright stain came out easily with some warm water.

"You can't go home in a wet dress," she said, and sat down to think.

Then she ran in next door with the dress, and, when she reappeared a good while later, the garment was totally dry. "Mrs

Doyle has an old salon hair-dryer," she explained, and maybe I imagined her adding, "No need for your mammy to know anything about this."

At home I never mentioned a thing and when my mother asked, "Did you have a good day?" I smiled and said, "The best!" And meant it. Everything had gone to plan.

When I was growing up our relationship was at best cautious and uneasy. My mother could change the happy mood of a day in an instant. She had a hair-trigger temper and was quick to take offence where none was intended and we were beyond each other's understanding.

But my First Communion was a day of rare harmony between us and as such is vividly remembered. It *was* perfect.

Ann Carroll is really a ten-year-old disguised as an adult (quite an old adult) and her aim is to recreate the vivid landscape of childhood for her readers through characters and adventures which are both humorous and gripping. She is the author of six books in the *Rosie* time-travel series and has also written *Amazing Grace*, the story of a nine-year-old who finds a magic comb, and *Laura Delaney's Deadliest Day*, the tale of an eleven-year-old who gets to be the fifth-class teacher for a day. Currently she is writing the Nutshell series of Irish Myths and Legends, for which Derry Dillon creates wonderful illustrations. All of her books are published by Poolbeg Press.

Back When the World Made Sense

Fiona Cassidy

Looking back on my formative years now, I know I led a charmed existence. I grew up with my parents as an only child in the rolling hills of Galbally in rural County Tyrone, a place I still call home. My parents were both teachers and for their sins both taught me in school, an experience which I look back on with fond memories and some amusement.

My father used to set "composition" assignments for his class where everyone was given a topic to write about and the author of the best-constructed piece of work was rewarded with the princely sum of twenty pence to spend in the local shop. I remember penning a particular masterpiece featuring a duck as the main character which earned me my twenty-pence reward but I took exception to the fact that the prize was presented to me at home where my father retained the title of "Daddy" and not "Sir" as I had to call him in school. The result of that particular disagreement was that he had to give me my money in front of the whole class the next day as my argument was that if I had earned it then everyone else should know how talented I was and never mind the fact that I was his daughter . . . leaving him worried about others thinking he was showing favouritism!

Mammy and Daddy adopted me when I was a week short of four months old and I'm like the queen as I have my official birthday on the 7th March but also have a mini-celebration on the 30th June as that is when I "came home" to them. I always knew that I was adopted as my parents were open and honest about the fact and that made life a lot easier for me as I had no shocks to deal with as a teenager. I used to conjure up romantic notions in my head as to why I had been given away and my birth mother used to be cast in the role of a variety of characters, each of whom would have had their own dramas to contend with! She would morph from a tragic heroine who had to float me up a river in a basket reminiscent of Moses, to a young mother who grew up on the shores of Summer Bay in Australia, to a lowly film-set employee who had a love child with Tom Cruise. *Top Gun* was one of my favourite films growing up and Tom Cruise was my favourite actor and I can remember squinting at the TV screen looking for similarities in our appearance and miraculously always managed to find some. The fact that he had dark eyes, dark hair and a huge nose and was an American citizen with no ties to Ireland didn't seem to dissuade me in my beliefs that my birth mother, whom I obviously favoured in looks, had had a passionate affair with him. It was such a shame that she ended up having to give her baby away but, as Hollywood contracts frowned on set staff fraternising in their dressing rooms with the main stars, she had no choice. Even at that early age I had an imagination that was inclined to run away with me so I suppose, to my parents at least, it was probably no surprise that their daughter would end up as a women's fiction author one day in the future.

When I was a child, life was simple and happy and good. Unfortunately at the time I probably interpreted that as being boring but now I value the carefree, safe and content bubble that was my world when growing up. My parents were always there for me. There was never any trouble in the house and neither one took it upon themselves to put anything or anyone in front of the precious child that had been bestowed upon them. I guess I was one of the lucky ones and if I had one wish I'd like to bring my own children to that place where everything was simple and as it should be in an ideal world.

In recent times, in particular, when life has been hard to bear, and thoughts of childhood and that safe place where no one could hurt me have been comforting, I've often thought of how lovely it would be to revert back to being a child again. How nice it would be to be the recipient of love and affection where someone else could take charge and control and be the oracle of all wisdom and knowledge that the role of being a parent brings with it. No one actually tells you when you give birth that as well as being a mammy you also take on the responsibility of being a multi-tasking octopus who holds the answers to all questions no matter how ridiculous or difficult they might be. I learnt in my fledging days as a mother that the answer "Because that's the way God made it" was a good response to most riddles and then my children could take up their confusing analogies with the Almighty as obviously it was His fault for making the sky blue and more bizarrely for making toes and hands go wrinkly in the bath, which was the source of a great amount of analysing and debate in our house.

A favourite childhood memory of mine involved helping to bring in the hay with my cousins who lived on a farm next door. My mother kept me looking like a porcelain doll with ringlets that Nellie Olesen from *Little House on the Prairie* would have been proud to sport the rest of the year, so part of the attraction of hay time to me was probably the fact that I could embrace my inner desire to be a tomboy and get mucky and dirty for a change. I used to love the sweet smell of the hay and climbing all over the bales and rolling down the hills after the grass had been cut. Mammy and Daddy would also have been there helping out and one of the biggest and most startling factors about them being involved was that it was the one and only time I can ever remember my mother wearing trousers. It stands to reason obviously that nylon tights would not survive a minute when faced with lugging about prickly bales of straw but in my wee head it was a novelty and therefore something to celebrate.

Even as a child I was an incorrigible bookworm who had an insatiable appetite for the latest Famous Five saga in Enid Blyton's repertoire. A real treat for me was to get picking the latest book in the collection from Jeffers book shop in Portadown where Mammy and Daddy would take me. We used to go out for "wee runs" in the car and Daddy would be pointing things out to me with regard to scenery or places of interest but then gave it up as a bad job when he realised that he was always addressing the top of my head which was permanently buried in a book.

I often find even now as an adult, if I'm ever getting it tough, that opening one of my childhood treasures brings great waves of comfort and consolation. I can still remember Mammy and Daddy reading excerpts from Enid Blyton's *Br'er Rabbit* books and chapters from *The Little House on the Prairie* books by Laura Ingalls Wilder. Those were a gift from my Aunt Ann who lived in St Louis Missouri. I was nine years old and still have them in the same presentation box to this day. I wish that my children had grown up in an era where there was less emphasis on gadgets and games and more reliance on books for fun.

As I was on my own I was in the privileged position of getting to choose a friend to go on holidays with Mammy and Daddy and me. There were trips to Bundoran and Rossnowlagh in Donegal and Salthill in Galway and then there was the amazing trip to America to visit my aunties and cousins when I was nine. My daddy often recalls our day out to the St Louis Arch on the 4th of July, American Independence Day, when it absolutely deluged and I announced in a very loud lispy Irish accent that the rain was wetter over here than at home and then couldn't understand why everyone had chuckled around me.

When I hit secondary school I went to St Joseph's Convent Grammar in Donaghmore. People will say that your schooldays are supposed to be the best days of your life whilst shuddering and making faces but in my case I found it to be true. Although I probably disliked homework and was the world's worst mathematician, I look back on my days at school with great fondness and only wish I had taken the time to appreciate them a bit more when I was actually there.

One of my biggest regrets is that I didn't keep a diary as a child. I often wish that I had kept a journal mapping out all the things I did, places visited and experiences had, and if I could go back in time that is one thing that I would be instructing my younger self to do. Along with that advice I'd be informing the young Fionnuala to be more careful in her life choices and not to allow a man to approach unless he was riding a white horse and answering to the name Charming! I'd also tell her to appreciate her parents a bit more as they were and are a couple in a million.

I'd love it if my children could experience the happy times that I had and also if they could see what life was like when people had less to live on but probably coped better than they do today, although prising my daughter away from her mobile phone and getting my son to step away from the XBox remote might just be pushing it. I think my younger children, however, would appreciate the outdoorsy approach to life when playing "let's pretend" was very real and sky was the blue canvas above us as opposed to a digital satellite dish.

I always remember the sense of wonder and delight that new places and experiences create when you're young and, given half a chance, I'd bottle that feeling and keep it forever as I think it's important no matter what age you are to retain a certain amount of awe about what's happening around you.

So basically I suppose what I'm saying is that if I had the chance to be a child again I'd like to be armed with the adult knowledge that you only ever get one shot at it and every moment is precious! I'd also like to congratulate my parents on a job well done and perhaps I'd elaborate on the "Tom Cruise is really my birth father" idea a bit more but, then again, maybe not as I don't think Scientology would be my cup of tea!

Children of the world – life is for living. Savour every moment and don't wish your childhood away, because once it's gone you'll never get those days back and some of us adults would literally give our eye teeth to have the chance to go back to a time when the world wasn't a scary place full of conundrums, difficult decisions and the sad but very real fact that sometimes the people you thought you could rely on the most are the ones who let you down the hardest! No, we'd like to go back to a time where the world actually made sense.

Fiona Cassidy is the bestselling author of *Anyone For Seconds?*, *Anyone For Me?* and *Anyone For Secrets?*. She also writes educational plays and has written a children's story. She facilitates creative writing workshops for adults, young people and children, and also delivers classes from a therapeutic perspective for trauma sufferers. She lives in Galbally, County Tyrone with her four children Colm, Úna, Áine and Orán.

Reflections

Carol Coffey

If for even just one day
I could be a child again
Yet take with me all I've learnt since
Into that world of innocence

If I could tell the younger me
Not to fret about what cannot be
That being so very, very small
Is not so terrible at all

If I could take her by the hand
And walk with her past the bully's stand
And try my best to make her see
That he is just as scared as she

Her fears I'd try to alleviate
Like Mother's rooster at the gate
And monsters in the long green mile
Will someday, I'd tell her, make her smile

I'd tell her to keep close to her heart
The happy times that made her laugh
For these sustain me every day
Through harder times that come my way

The laughter of my siblings' games
Cowboys and Indians in the rain
From Christmas mornings by the fire
To swinging on an old worn tyre

Before that lovely day would end
I'd tell the younger me again
The things that make her sad today
Will slow and dim and fade away

I'd say the things for which she aches
Will not a happy childhood make
The bike, the doll, the fancy clothes
Will not sustain her in the cold

And adolescence with all its woes
Will be more painful than she knows
Hopes and expectations raised
Crushed upon the light of day

But childhood dreams now worn and dashed
Will lead her down a different path
Where unexpected wants and wishes
Bring forth a different kind of riches

But I suspect that even if
That day could be conferred on me
My younger self will not be told
Or listen to one so very old

Reflections

For this journey she must make alone
Decisions on the winding road
Its twists and turns, its knocks and dents
The richness of those life events

And finally before I'd leave
That little child would smile at me
And ask why I no longer watch the sky
Or count the passing clouds go by

Why I don't take picnics in the rain
Or jump in puddles in the lane
Why there's no sparkle in my eye
And why on earth I've stopped saying "Why?"

And with those words we make a pact
On her advice I now will act
To keep my counsel I will vow
For she knows more than I know now

She knows to laugh and live and smile
And move through life with open eyes
And open heart and soul and mind
Her eyes trained forward – not behind.

Carol Coffey was born in Dublin and after a ten-year stay in Australia has settled in County Wicklow. She has a degree in Education and a Master's Degree in Behavioural Disturbance. She is a teacher by profession and continues to work in the area of special education. She has written four novels, all published by Poolbeg. Carol has used her extensive background working with children with disabilities to bring the world of special needs to the wider population through her writing. Her first novel, *The Butterfly State*, published in 2009, centres on a young autistic girl. *The Penance Room* is set in outback Australia and provides an insight into the isolated world of the deaf child, while *Winter Flowers,* set in Dublin, examines the generational effects of dysfunctional upbringings on parents and their children. Her most recent novel, *The Incredible Life of Jonathan Doe*, examines the life of an amnesic man living in a homeless shelter in America and challenges our notions of identity and the importance of finding out who we are and where we belong.

Bells, Bibles, Lupins and Love

Roslyn Dee

Some childhoods last longer than others. Some are quickly gone, consigned to the past for all sorts of reasons, while others can be summoned up at a moment's notice, hey-presto-like, as if by magic. And even when you least expect it.

For a childhood is an ephemeral thing, hovering somewhere out there on the edge of memory, little droplets of remembrance that flit across the consciousness from time to time, triggered by a scent, perhaps, or a specific colour, an old film, a piece of jewellery, or maybe by something as random as the faded pattern on a china cup you happen upon in one of those "vintage" shops. Touchstones, all of them, for a time that is itself trapped in time.

For me it's many things – Pears soap, the LP cover of *South Pacific*, the voice of Jim Reeves on my parents' first turntable, Camp coffee, *Perry Mason* on television, Midget Gem sweets, the tune "Santa Lucia" (emitted from my mother's gondola-shaped music box), pink "John Church" roses, dahlias, Donegal . . . All random hallmarks, fragments of a long-ago memory that instantly roots me in my past.

And when my mind wanders there, searching in that

hinterland of my early life, dredging the seabed of my memory, it is to my grandparents' house that my thoughts inevitably turn. If I could step through a CS Lewis-style wardrobe, right now, today, I'd choose to find myself there with the two of them, in the small front room of the terraced house where they lived their long and happy lives together.

It's more than half a century since my mother's parents first became so central to my world. And twenty-one years now since Jeanie, aged ninety-two, took leave of this life, the sixteen years of widowhood without her Johnny finally over. "Go on, you old fool," she used to say to him in her quiet way when he, much more gregarious and expressive, would turn on his gentle charm and make her smile.

Always together. Always in harmony. A marriage, celebrated at the end of the Great War, that, despite their different temperaments and an age gap of almost a decade between them, endured way past the fall of Saigon. Till death did them part.

In their home on the Long Commons in Coleraine they made their life – John Dean, my grandfather, being from the locality and she, Jeanie Bradley, reared beyond the town, in the family cottage that sat along the seashore near Magilligan, that County Derry stretch of the Atlantic that sweeps dramatically around the northern tip of this island. The majestic crags of Binevenagh mountain overhang the coast here, the Mussenden Temple (that godsend landmark for every Northern Ireland Tourist Board campaign) sits high on the cliffs at nearby Downhill, Derry city lies less than twenty miles distant, and the hills of Donegal beckon from just across the choppy waters.

It was a life that revolved around my mother, their adored only child. Later, the net widened to include her handsome young husband. Then next into that family fold came my sister and finally, eight years after her arrival, it was my time.

It all seems so long ago now, that close-knit, happy childhood of mine. And yet I only have to glance around the bedroom I share with my husband today and I'm back there – right back in Jeanie and Johnny Dean's living room.

For there on my dressing-table is my granny's little trinket box; over there, by the door, is that low-seated "nursing" chair, re-upholstered now in a different fabric, but still intact; and just there, on the windowsill, where the sunlight glints off it, is a cream and gold ornament, shaped like an opened book and with the words of The Lord's Prayer, now somewhat faded, inscribed on it. If I close my eyes I can still picture it on the top shelf of the bow-fronted glass cabinet in that front room of theirs.

It's fitting, indeed, that the Lord's Prayer ornament should have survived the passage of time, for Jeanie and Johnny lived their lives under the benevolent shadow of their church – St Patrick's, on the main street of Coleraine, and just a two-minute stroll from the Long Commons.

It was there that my grandfather sang in the choir as a young man, there that he attended the Boys' Brigade and there too that, for over fifty years, he rang the bells every Sunday morning, a master of the art of campanology. Oh, the thrill of being taken by the hand up to the belfry, that magical place from where the call to prayer was sounded every week, the assembled bellringers led by my granda's expert hands. Full circle ringing, the clapper, the full peal, the muffled peal . . . the language of the art form that is bellringing still has resonances for me all these decades later.

For Granny, meanwhile, her godly contribution was a commitment to weekly worship, always in Pew Number 101, and to her midweek women's Bible Class meetings, as much a female get-together, I suspect, as a religious meeting of minds. A chance for the women of the house to escape for a few hours and talk about things that, way back then, held no interest for their menfolk. A kind of before-its-time, all-girls book club – minus the Merlot, of course.

And so it was that Sunday School and weekly church attendance became part of the fabric of my childhood. With my own mother up-front in the choir stalls, and my granda, fresh from his belfry endeavours, having slipped into the bellringers' pew at the back of the church just as the service began, it was with my granny that I sat on many a Sunday morning. Years later, when I returned on university holidays from England, and later again, when visiting from my Dublin home, I'd often pitch up at St Patrick's and slip in beside my granny in Pew 101, my church-filled childhood flooding back over me. The enduring power of ritual.

And that ritual was not just confined to Sundays. When I was five or six and attending primary school my grandfather was already retired. My granny did occasional work but was largely home-based and so I enjoyed that most blessed of gifts – close proximity, on a daily basis, to both my grandparents. School was a five-minute walk from their house and every day, when I emerged from the confines of the low-rise, red-brick Irish Society school buildings, there he'd be at the school gates – my granda. An erect, handsome, grey-haired figure, with a gentleness about him and a smile never far from his lips, he was easy to pick out as he stood there, chatting to all the assembled mothers waiting to collect their offspring.

Then down we'd go to Long Commons, in through the door of Number 47, in to Granny, and to whatever treat awaited me. And then, fed and watered (and, if it was a Thursday – pension day – having received a shilling for myself), off Granda and I would go, heading for my own house on the Portstewart Road, one of the main residential roads leading out of the town to the coast.

A long walk? Not really. At a brisk pace we're talking fifteen, twenty minutes, tops. But for me and my grandfather it was a daily ramble, an odyssey of sorts, and so it became a journey that could take us up to an hour.

"Give me that schoolbag, daughter," he'd say. "You can't be carrying that on your back – you'll be all humped up!" And so he'd relieve me of what he considered my back-breaking burden and we'd walk and chat, chat and walk. Down Brook Street, past the church hall, up the incline in the road, Circular Road off to the right now, heading for the crossroads at Union Street, me skipping along and he greeting passers-by and the townspeople he knew on the way. Time for a pit-stop – so into the little shop on the left-hand side of the road before the crossroads for a quarter of Midget Gems, perhaps, or some other such sweetie delight.

Then on we'd go, over what was (and is still, in our family) known as the Tip Head. Then past the playing field and along by the hawthorn hedgerow with the "secret" path behind it. In there I'd vanish, only to emerge to "surprise" Granda, and he, content to humour me, never tiring of playing along with my childish imaginings. No, he'd tell me, somewhat appalled, when I'd want to pull the full-bloom hawthorn to carry home for my mother and father returning later from work. "No," he'd say, shaking his head. "You couldn't bring hawthorn into the house, child – it's bad luck."

Back in the Long Commons, meanwhile, behind my grandparents' house and just outside the gate of their backyard, a laneway ran along the backs of the terrace of houses. On the other side of that laneway each house had its own small garden. An oasis on a summer's day, theirs was the first place I ever encountered lupins, grown in profusion along the back wall there – in pinks and purples and pale yellows – by my green-fingered grandmother.

She loved flowers, as her own mother had done before her, and her daughter after her. It's a family addiction that has passed down along the female gene – a Bradley birthright of sorts. Indeed, lupins are still one of my favourite summer flowers – as they were Granny's. And peony roses, those beauties of vibrant cerise that appear in early summer, fading to palest pink before death overcomes them. "Piney" roses my great-grandmother called them, so my mother tells me, when she grew them in her cottage garden in Magilligan. Now, in my parents' garden – in the same house that my granda walked me home to after school half a century ago – peonies still bloom in the shelter of the wall every summer.

There were daisies aplenty too, of course, in that Long Commons garden, and it was there that I first learned from my granda how to make a daisy-chain. Years later, when he was a very old man, he was still at it, making daisy-chains for the youngsters who then lived nearby. "I can't come in for my dinner yet," he called to my granny one day when she called him in to eat. "I'm making a daisy-chain for Joanne." When he died, aged eighty-five, not long after that, a delicate spray of flowers from little Joanne rested on his coffin.

Beyond the garden in Long Commons lay the children's playground – within sight of the back lane but far enough removed to feel like freedom. I played there, naturally, the swings and slide and roundabout all magnets in any childhood. But, to be honest, I wasn't seeking freedom, for I was far too happy being inside with my grandparents in the bosom of Number 47.

Fragments of those long-ago, day-to-day memories still linger. Granny pulling out the armchair to put a shilling in the gas meter concealed by a curtain behind it, pottering around, a petite, apron-clad figure, in the scullery or the back room, doing her daily chores. Making Camp coffee on occasion, a real treat in a tea-drinking household – pouring the dark brown chicory-flavoured liquid from that distinctive bottle, heating up the milk (she always made it completely with milk) and carrying in the steaming hot cups for the two of us.

Granda, meanwhile, sitting by a torcher of a fire on a winter's afternoon, *Perry Mason* on the television perhaps, or some other detective drama that had him captivated. In summer, however, in the late sixties and early seventies, there was no escape from Wimbledon. He loved it, as he loved all sports, and I'd sit with him as he'd watch, riveted, from his armchair, as the shots sizzled back and forth across Centre Court. The Australian star Rod Laver was in his heyday back then and the British player, Virginia Wade, was coming into her own – "Mr Laver" and "Miss Wade" my grandfather always called them, slightly in awe. Ever the gentleman.

Certain childhoods last longer than others. And some, where the good ghosts of yesteryear still live so vividly in our memories, last a lifetime.

Roslyn Dee is Associate Editor of the *Irish Daily Mail* and the *Irish Mail on Sunday* and formerly Assistant Editor of the *Sunday Tribune*. An award-winning travel writer and broadcaster, she is joint author, with her photographer husband, Gerry Sandford, of A *Sense of Place: Irish Lives, Irish Landscapes*. She was the editor of *Who We Are: A Collection of Essays on Life in Contemporary Ireland*, published by New Island in 2010.

A Letter to my Future Teenagers

Caroline Finnerty

There isn't too much that I would change about my early childhood years. In fact, I had a pretty idyllic childhood, almost to the point of cliché. When we weren't in school, our days were spent exploring fields and jumping ditches and not returning home until it was dusk. It was all fancy paper, *Glenroe* on a Sunday night, picking our favourite Rose of Tralee from their profiles in the *RTÉ Guide*, Coke floats and SodaStreams. But one minute everything was hunky-dory and then somewhere at around the age of twelve, it wasn't quite so rosy any more.

You see my memories of the latter part of my childhood are mainly of a young girl who was plagued with huge doubts and full of desperate insecurities about herself. I wasn't quite sure where I fitted in or where I belonged. I was so self-conscious of every little thing as I tried to find my footing in the transition between childhood and adulthood. Some days I wanted to grow up faster than my body could grow, pushing the boundaries and the limits, and other days I wished I could go back to the uncomplicated days of playing with my Barbies and reading my Famous Five books.

I was good in school and had always been studious but I started to lose interest at around the age of fifteen. I could see teachers grow frustrated with me. They knew I was very capable but I think I thought it was cooler not to try. I also fought a lot with my parents, over and over again. My mother always says I was such an easy child but I more than made up for it as a teenager. If I could go back to being a child again for one more day let's just say that those teen years wouldn't exactly be at the top of my time-travel list but if you *forced* me to go back there (that is, dragged me back kicking and screaming), I think I would have a little pep talk with myself and tell the younger me that it really does get better and to cheer up and ditch the green hairband. I would also be much kinder to my parents because now that I'm a mother myself I can appreciate how hard it must have been for them dealing with me and my ungrateful strops.

Some people are lucky and will sail through their teenage years without too much carnage and I, like all parents, hope that my children will be like that. But, just in case, this is a letter to my future teenagers:

To My Future Teenagers

When you came into this world, my life was forever changed – in the best possible way. We changed your nappies, worried when you had a temperature, held your hand on your first day of school, and now you've reached that age where we are a source of mortifying embarrassment and you don't want to be around us any more. If you're anything like I was at the same age, you're probably not even talking to me right now. I know you would rather listen to your friends than us and that's normal, but I thought I would write down some advice for you based on my own memories of being a teenager and also of things that I have learnt along the way. Who knows, it might be useful to you and if not you can always use the paper to doodle on. Here it goes . . .

A Letter to my Future Teenagers

When I think back to myself at your age I hated everything about how I looked and, although you are perfect in my eyes, I know that you probably think that you have bad teeth/spotty skin or that you are too tall/too short (tick as appropriate). Unless you are really lucky, you will probably find something you obsess over. But guess what, whatever it is that you are insecure about, is a big deal only to you. The chances are that everyone else is too busy worrying about their own issues to really pay too much attention to yours. You don't know this now but I promise you one day you will look back on photos of yourself from this time and wish that you had appreciated yourself more. And no, you are not fat, so stop obsessing about your weight.

Friends are important so if you find a true friend, who loves you for you, realise how lucky you are and hold onto them with both hands. If a friend doesn't make you feel good about yourself then maybe you need to rethink whether they really are your friend after all. And if someone says something spiteful about you, remember they are showing up their own insecurities – the only reason people say bitchy or mean things is because they are jealous of something that you have. Use that knowledge to your advantage, but it also has a flipside – if you find yourself badmouthing others or excluding someone, use it to see what you are lacking or are worried about in yourself. Nasty behaviour is like an inward mirror, so be careful about what it is reflecting.

Pursue a sport or hobby – yes, I know I'm a hypocrite as I'm the least sporty person I know and the girl who begged for a note to get out of PE (you can ask your nanny about that one) but it doesn't have to be a sport. You can help a charity, join a drama group, play music or even write, like me. Whatever it is, it is good to have an interest outside of school. When I ask other adults about how they found their teenage years, it is usually the ones who played a sport or had a hobby they loved who came through relatively unscathed.

I really don't mind what you do when you grow up, as long as:
a) It makes you happy
b) You can make a living out of it

and

c) It is legal.

So go after something you are passionate about and put your heart and soul into it. You're going to have to put yourself out there – you will feel exposed and vulnerable but you have to take a risk. Yes, you might get knocked but it also might just happen. And if it turns out that you do fail, then you have learnt something that you didn't know before and you'll be a step closer to achieving your dream. I would rather you took a risk and went after something than played it safe, never to realise your potential. Go after it while you're young because, once you have the responsibilities of a mortgage or children, the stakes get even higher. It doesn't matter if you don't know what to do with your life after school. Sometimes you have to take the long way around so enjoy the journey and trust you will arrive there. As the saying goes: "Do something you love and you'll never work a day in your life." And don't worry about what other people are doing – you have no power over other people, so it is futile. But what you can control is yourself, so just put that energy into that and it will all turn out fine.

Love is the same. Sometimes you have to let down your barriers in order to let love in. It can be scary opening yourself up to another person but if the feeling is reciprocated you won't regret it. Don't let Hollywood cloud your expectations of relationships: they take work. Don't cast it aside if it's broken, try to fix it first. Be kind to one another; romance is a two-way street – you get back what you put in. And, yes, I know you are going to have sex one day but please wait until you are old enough to choose wisely. Sex is a complicated, emotional thing, not to be given away easily or casually thrown around. Make sure it is with someone who loves you and cherishes you. Pressure isn't love. If there is one thing as a parent that I can give you it would be that you would value yourself as much as I value you. Without going all Oprah* on you, if you love and respect yourself, others will treat you that way too. And for my son, always respect the wishes of the girl you are with. And all of you, please be responsible!

Smile even when you don't feel like it. You look better that way and people will be more receptive to you. Try it – it's contagious.

There will come a time when I won't be there with you and you will have your own choices to make and I have to trust that I raised you to make the right decision. There will be times when it will be easier to follow the crowd. When everyone is going one way, it can be hard to turn against the tide and go your own way, but listen to your gut – if something doesn't feel right then it probably isn't.

You'll be glad to know that I'm nearly finished but the last thing I want to say to you is that I hope we will always talk. You might feel as though your music understands you in a way no one else ever can (in my day the band was Radiohead in case you're interested). You may not imagine that I as your mother could possibly know what you are going through but although things are different for teenagers nowadays, the same worries, pressures, doubts and insecurities still exist. The one thing that we have in common is our feelings and I don't think those things will ever change for teenagers. So if you are finding things difficult at the moment, I just want to say that it does get better, I promise. You are only at the start of your journey; there are a lot of exciting things in store for you. And lastly, as Oscar Wilde sums up perfectly: "Be yourself; everyone else is already taken." You are perfect exactly as you are; there is no one more beautiful than you.

My love always,
Mom xxx

* If you are wondering who the hell is Oprah, she was a talk-show queen in the nineties and one of the richest women in America – Google her.

Caroline Finnerty lives on the banks of the Grand Canal in County Kildare with her husband, three young children and their dog. A graduate of NUI Maynooth and the Michael Smurfit Business School, she worked in the retail pharmacy sector for many years before giving up the corporate world after her twins were born in 2011. Her first book *In a Moment* was published in April 2012, her second *The Last Goodbye* in July 2013. As well as compiling *If I Was a Child Again*, she is also working on her third novel. She has had articles published in *Woman's Way, The Star, The Daily Mail* as well as various parenting magazines. You can find out more on her website www.carolinefinnerty.ie or she can be found on Twitter as @cfinnertywriter.

Sunshine, Short Socks and School Dinners

Vanessa Fox O'Loughlin

What are your memories of school? I wonder if the pictures in your head are the same as mine?

Like Polaroid snaps, I see partial images – blurred at the edges, someone's shoulder obscuring the shot, the back of someone else's head; but like Polaroids, my memories are full colour. Some of my earliest childhood memories are of Skyswood School in St Albans, Hertfordshire, where I grew up. They are disjointed and patchy, like someone tipped the album upside down and the memories floated out of it, landing in a jumble on the floor, but as I sort through them to write this I know they are all very happy, and now I come to think of it, in almost every one of them, the sun is shining.

I started primary school when Carl Douglas was "Kung Fu Fighting" and the Osmonds were hot on his heels with "Love Me For A Reason", Harold Wilson's Labour government was struggling through recession and Ford made the ill-fated decision to pardon Nixon. It was the year of *The Man with the Golden Gun* and *The Towering Inferno*. At five years old my memories are more of yellow cars and platform lace-ups, of the roughness of the carpet in the reading corner, the tables in the infant classroom that were just the right size for me.

What else? First-day nerves dissolved by the discovery of wonderful folders full of words. With orange card covers they opened to reveal slots for little white slips of card printed in bold black type. The Word folders were magical to me, contained the building blocks of sentences, sentences that were to form and reform and open the door to the world of reading and writing – and books. I devoured *Roger Red Hat* and *Billy Blue Hat*, reading one every night. And then the comprehension books came, their edges soft with use, covers asymmetric designs in green, white and black. Packed full of stories with questions to answer, 1 to 10 – hardly work at all.

Often we walked to school, up the steep cut from Sandpit Lane past the horse's field to a road lined with cherry trees, laden with blossom. I'm holding Mum's hand as we stream across the playground heading in to school. The other children are all bigger than me in my bobble hat and winter coat. Who is laughing in the group ahead of us? One of the girls has put on her tights but forgotten to put on her knickers! Her tights are bottle green, her coat grey. The image is hazy but the laughter real.

But that is spring, and most of the pictures from the album in my head are of summer – of blue gingham dresses and lacy white cotton socks, honeysuckle tumbling over the wall behind the senior classrooms, bees buzzing – was there a pond? Hanging upside down on the metal climbing frame, all in a row, swinging from our knees. Daddy Longlegs on the wooden wall of the "hut", a prefab classroom, and inside, that unique hut smell, the sound of our feet on the hollow floor, the spring of the lino, the smell of chalk and dusty blackboards, the excitement of having a lesson somewhere new.

Jumping rhymes and elastics in the playground; and our cycling proficiency, wobbling around the bollards on my huge old-fashioned bike. The years are mixed up, like faded cine film flicking from scene to scene.

And who were the other children in my class? I can see them

clearly – in Mrs Cooke's classroom. Anita newly arrived from Cornwall, her dark curls bent over her knitting needles as her fingers flew, producing tiny knitted mice with faces so lifelike their noses twitched. And Diane – do you remember us listening to Adam and The Ants' "Prince Charming" on the tape machine in your bedroom? Mark, whose Dad worked on an oil rig, and Leigh whose family was from Malta. Holly who had terrified my mother when we were in nursery school with her huge and very real boa-constrictor snake. We didn't have pets until years later, so the memories of people's animals are mixed up with my memories of them. Holly had a cat that slept under her covers on her bed, Maxine had fabulous and fearsome Alsatian dogs. Tiny Jane with her straight dark hair had the most coveted pet of all: a horse.

And my teachers? Singing "Kookaburra" with Mrs Steadman from New Zealand, who hooked her long hair behind her ears and wore long patterned skirts; "Kumbaya" and learning all about Kiwis.

Mrs Woodhead, Mr Peppin in his brown polyester suits and Mr Cliff who sharpened his chalk to a point to produce the most beautiful script on the blackboard. Mrs Cooke, whose brother was part of the St Ives lifeboat crew in Cornwall, and who took us all to the Isle of Wight for a week's holiday in our last year of school. Needlework with Mrs Green, and finding a piece of fur fabric with *Squirrel* written on the back that had our little group collapsing in hysterics.

The highlights: 1977 and the Queen's Jubilee, a long, hot summer with water shortages, the grass on the field parched, the ground baked hard; getting dressed up for the fête (as what, I've no idea!) and the precious Silver Jubilee coin in its blue-and-silver plastic cover.

And that Isle of Wight trip, the first trip away from home. Sharing a room with Diane, Maxine and Jane, hot cocoa in the evenings and the outdoor swimming pool, water freezing. Going out each morning on the coach with our lunch in a clear plastic bag, seeing peacocks and water wheels and Osbourne House.

This holiday began my love of project work, of research, collecting all the scraps of information together into a record of the trip.

My memories of Skyswood School, of treacle and chocolate sponges with lashings of thick custard, of watching safety films in the dining room, the windows blacked out; of wonderful school plays, the atmosphere backstage serious and alive with excitement, are like scraps in a project, photos in an album. But so much more than just a collection of memories, Skyswood gave me a love of learning and a love of words that began on that first page of my colourful album of memories, with short socks and sunshine and school dinners.

Vanessa Fox O'Loughlin is the founder of the Irish national writing resources website www.writing.ie and The Inkwell Group publishing consultancy. She is a literary scout who has assisted many authors to publication. She conceived and developed the National Emerging Writer Programme for Dublin City of Literature, and is currently working with WritersWebTV.com bringing free, live, online workshops to writers worldwide. She is the Vice Chair of Irish PEN and the Irish and Eurozone Adviser to the international Alliance of Independent Authors. She regularly talks about writing and getting published on Sunshine 106.8fm's *Andrea Hayes' Saturday Morning Show Live*. Vanessa has been writing fiction since 1999 when her husband set sail across the Atlantic for eight weeks and she had an idea for a book.

Silvermints

Sorcha Furlong

Friday evenings were always the best nights in our house when me and my sister were little. We used to wait with bated breath for my dad to come home from work. Not only did we miss him like mad 'cos he was a sales rep and he could be gone most weeks from Monday to Friday, but we loved to see him rock in the door with the two brown-paper bags full of goodies! I'm sure you could see the drool rolling down from our mouths!

He wouldn't be even in the door and he'd have the two of us jumping up on him.

And never more eagerly than the evening I had my special plan . . .

"Daddy! Have you got anything for us?"

He knows by the twinkle in our eyes what we mean. "Eh, no, nothing . . . just me!" (My dad the messer!)

"Daddy, come on, it's Friday and you *always* get us our bag of goodies on Fridays!" (I'm eight now so I know what I'm talking about!)

"Oh no, is it Friday?" he says with the most innocent look on his face.

Louisa is only five and her lips begin to quiver. I put a reassuring arm around her ('cos I am eight!). I realise that poor Lou is falling for his act – she's getting sucked in – but I know he's only messing – he *is* only messing, right? He couldn't have forgotten our goodies on a Friday? He has *never* forgotten our goodies on a Friday . . . oh, nooooo, my Silvermints!

"Mmmmmyyyyy Silvermints!"

Okay, calm down, keep it together – you are eight! Okay so, what does an eight-year-old do in this situation, when their father is holding their sweets hostage? Answer . . . simple!

"*Mam! Mammy!*" (Tricia Furlong, the peacekeeper!)

"David, will you just give the girls their sweets, and stop antagonising them!" (Of course we have *nooo* idea what that big word means, but we know who the boss is, and it isn't Daddy!)

Dad smiles and looks down at his two little girls, who are looking back up at him hoping and praying that he is only messing. "Well . . . I suppose I haven't checked my suitcase yet – maybe they're in there?"

The sentence isn't even finished before me and Lou are on the suitcase like bees to honey.

"Okay, okay, girls, calm down! I'll get them for you." Dad opens the case – slowly, of course! – and lifts out our sugar fix.

There they are! Happy Friday to me! We grab them and begin to race up the stairs to our bedroom.

"Hang on, girls, have you anything you want to say to your dad?" says the voice of reason.

"Yeah! Thanks, Daddy, love you!"

We continue up the stairs, and as I am on the last step I glance back, to see my mam and dad in an embrace.

"I missed you," he says tenderly.

Mam smiles. "Me too."

They kiss. I smile.

Okay, so if you were to ask me now who the brains of the family is I would say my sister. We are now in our thirties, and she is someone I admire and love immensely. (Yes, Andrew, I love and admire you too, but you weren't born for this memory!) Okay, so like I was saying, Louisa is the brains of the operation *now*, but back then I was the big sister and she was only five, so she had to do everything I said. Because I knew everything. I was eight (have I mentioned that?).

So we race into our bedroom with our bags of sweets. Our bedroom is a typical eighties-style room: two single beds, princess pink curtains (man, I loved them!), Barbies everywhere! Barbie car, Barbie bed with glowing, yes, *glowing* sheets, Barbie kitchen, Barbie stable – every little girl's dream!

Anyway, I am on a mission! I have watched my prey for a few weeks and seen her routine. I know what little system she has, and *this* is the evening I'll put my plan into action. So, as Louisa spills her entire bag of sweets onto the carpet I know what she'll pick up first: chocolate white mice! You see, when Dad would get us the bags of sweets, he'd always get each of us the *same* sweets so there would be no arguments – 'cos, as every parent knows, there's nothing worse than listening to your child having a tantrum because one child has something that the other child wants. So Dave Furlong had it sussed: get them the same sweets so there are no arguments. *Go, Dave . . . easy!* Well, Dave, not tonight. Tonight daughter Number 1 is going to bring that theory tumbling down!

Chocolate white mice are Louisa's favourites – I mean, I think they're okay, but my favourites are Silvermints – I *lurve* Silvermints! So, as I spill my bag of sweets onto the carpet they are my first port of call. I brush by my chocolate white mice and the packet of Love Hearts. I grab my beloved Silvermints. I've waited all week for these babies so I open them as fast as I can. I love the smell that hits you the minute you open the silver paper. I'd shove two or three in at a time, and before I knew it the packet would be gone! The disappointment! I'd always wished that I could make them last longer, but until this day I was never able to do it, but today I have a plan.

I look over at Lou and she is on her Love Hearts – next on

her hit list will be the Silvermints.

Innocently chewing on "Be Mine" or whatever statement was on her Love Heart, Louisa looks at her big sis and gives a smile. This is it, this is my time, it's now or never, I think, so here goes . . .

"Louisa?"

"Yeah?" says the little innocent five-year-old.

"Do you wanna play a game?"

"Oh, okay. What kind of game?" She begins to open her packet of Silvermints.

"Eh, it's called 'Mass', and it's the coolest game ever!" I am fixated on her packet of Silvermints.

"Mass? How do you play it?" She places her first Silvermint in her mouth.

"Well, someone has to be the priest and the other person has to be the audience, and the priest has to give them Holy Communion."

She's about to reach for Silvermint number two and I'm in a cold sweat.

"Oh, okay. And who's going to be the priest?" she asks.

"Well, I should be because I'm the oldest. But if you like you can be the priest." I give her the big-sister smile.

"Okay," she says as she puts Silvermint two in her gob!

"Okay, so you'll be the priest and I'll pretend to be different people coming up for Holy Communion – so you just stand over there and I'll give you this . . ." I grab a bowl from our tea set.

"What's this for?" she asks as she inspects the bowl.

"It's for the Holy Communion," I answer.

"Oh, and what will we use for Holy Communion?"

I'm sure you all know by now where I'm going with this story, but poor Lou didn't.

"Oh, good question! What will we use for Holy Communion? Emmm . . ." My best acting ever was used on this evening! "We *could* use your Silvermints . . . 'cos they're white and round just like real Holy Communion!"

I stare at Louisa. She stares back.

There is silence. Is she buying it?

"Oh, okay then," she says.

Sold! To the lying eight-year-old!

I race around the room trying to set the scene for our "Mass" game. I take our bedroom lockers and put them between the beds then I push the beds to each side of the room and put the two lockers together. So that is Louisa's altar!

Then I kneel in front of the altar.

"Okay, I'm ready!"

I'm soooo excited. In two seconds I'll be sucking on a Silvermint!

Louisa stands in front of our altar with the bowl of Silvermints and I explain that all she has to do is hold out the Silvermint as Holy Communion, say "Body of Christ" and when I say "Amen" put the Silvermint in my mouth. And then I'll get up, walk to the back of the bedroom and walk back up as a different person, with a different walk, and a different voice! Genius, if I do say so myself!

Man, woman, boy, girl, I had it all sussed, and Louisa was laughing away at all my impersonations – my plan had worked!

As I walk up pretending to be an old man, Louisa is in stitches. She puts her hand into the bowl and then she realises that all the Silvermints are gone.

"Ah well, sure we can play it again next week!" I say with my belly full and satisfied.

Everything is perfect, the plan has worked. Not only did I get to eat my own packet but I got to eat Louisa's too, and if she doesn't cop on I can keep this game going for weeks and weeks! V.I.C.T.O.R.Y!

"Okay, we better get this room back to normal," I say.

I look at Lou and see her staring into the bowl . . . and then it happens. *The Lip!* We used to call her "Louie the Lip" 'cos the bottom lip would just start going if she was about to have a meltdown (something my own daughter has inherited).

Uh-oh, I'm in trouble!

"I've *noooo* Silvermints left!"

The Lip was in full action! My first reaction was "Okay,

okay, Lou – listen – we just played a game and you used them as Holy Communion, remember? 'Cos you were the priest." My speech is getting quicker and quicker, 'cos now I'm in a blind panic! I smile and try to calm her down.

"*You ate all my Silvermints!*" she bawled.

"Okay, Lou, I'm sorry – here, have my chocolate mice – look – they're your favourite!"

I dart over to where the mice are and land back beside her, trying to stop the crying by tempting her with the mice.

"*Noooooo, I want mmmmyyyyyy Silvermints!*"

And then it happens . . . the creaking on the stairs.

"What's going on up there?" Dad shouts.

"Eh, nothing!" I answer.

"Doesn't sound like nothing to me," he says, and before I can answer, Louisa legs it past me out onto the landing and straight down the stairs and into Dad's arms.

Ah man, I'm dead! I follow her out.

"Well?" Dad's looking up at me for an answer.

I'm frozen standing at the top of the stairs.

"We were just playing a game called Mass and we used Louisa's Silvermints as Holy Communion, and now she's crying 'cos they're all gone."

Dad is a little confused. "Louisa, why are you crying? You were only playing a game."

"Sorcha ate all my Silvermints!" she says through snot and tears.

"What do you mean, she ate all your Silvermints? Sorcha, what does Lou mean?"

I lower my head and tell my dad that Lou was the priest and she was giving me Holy Communion and I was playing different people.

"Well, you give Lou your packet of Silvermints then," he says as he begins to dry little Lou's tears.

"I can't," I say in a whisper.

"What do you mean, you can't?"

"Well, I ate mine already."

Dad puts Louisa down and looks up at me.

"Are you telling me that you ate *your own* packet of Silvermints *and* your sister's?"

I'm in trouble now!

"Yes," I say.

Louisa begins to cry again as if she's reliving the whole experience scene by scene. So Dad has one daughter at the top of the stairs who's been greedy and conniving, and another at the bottom of the stairs bawling as if her world just ended . . .

So what does he do . . . ?

"*Tricia!*" he calls.

Mam comes out into the hall. "What is going on out here?" she says.

Dad proceeds to tell her about the whole incident. I still have the head lowered and my puppy-dog eyes on standby.

"Right," says Mam, very matter of fact.

"Louisa, I'm going to buy you your own packet of Silvermints tomorrow. And Sorcha, I can't believe that you would do something so mean to your little sister. You are eight and should be setting an example for Louisa. I am so sad that you would do something like this."

I felt terrible!

She continued. "So as punishment you won't be getting any goodies on a Friday or any other day for two weeks."

She takes Louisa up in her arms and the three of them stare up at me and then go into the sitting room.

There I am, left standing at the top of the stairs, the outsider, the Silvermint thief. I feel absolutely gutted and ashamed – and slightly sick, 'cos I just overdosed on Silvermints.

So for two weeks I didn't get my goodies, and then on week three when I got the goody bag and my Silvermints I now sucked instead of biting so they lasted longer.

Lesson learnt!

Sorcha Furlong is best known for playing Orla Kirwan on RTÉ's *Fair City*, and is also a founding member and creative director of Smart Blondes productions. She is the mother of a three-year-old little girl called Stella. She was delighted when asked to get involved in this worthwhile project with Poolbeg and Barnardos. It is the *first* story she has ever written, never mind had published, and she hopes you enjoy reading it as much as she enjoyed writing it!

Te Quiero Todavia

Ciara Geraghty

It was the summer of 1985. The summer the Anglo-Irish Agreement was signed. The summer Bob Geldof leapt from his couch and tried to change the world. The summer the Rainbow Warrior sank. The summer Boris Becker became the youngest player ever to win Wimbledon and made tennis fans of us all.

Oh, and Greenland left the European Union.

Greenland? I know, me neither.

That was the summer I turned fifteen.

The summer I fell in love.

My New Romantic era was tapering off, although I continued to sport a Nick Rhodes haircut and could still play – with two fingers – "Tainted Love" on my synthesiser.

It happened one morning in June; which seems strange now, given that love seems more suited to the soft glow of evening rather than the bright glare of eleven a.m. on a Tuesday. I was in the Scout Den, a further oddity, when you consider I knew none of the words of "Ging Gang Goolie" and the closest I got to rope knots was the double one I used on the laces of my brand new Doc Martens.

Still, there I was. With my friend Elly. I was always with Elly.

We were like conjoined twins back then, united in our efforts to run with the local cool crowd in spite of the fact that we didn't attend the local secondary, climbing instead aboard the wheezing diesel train at Malahide station and taking the tracks less travelled to Raheny, where we attended Manor House, which was considered posher (we wore gym knickers when we played hockey and had 'indoor' shoes) and nerdier (we did O levels in transition year instead of setting up companies and volunteering at Meals On Wheels), with the added horror of its single-sex status. This desertion to a different school made outsiders of us in our home town. We were as exposed as the stout Americans who came to search for their roots, dressed for golf.

My red hair didn't help. The colour of a bag of carrots back then. Titian, my mother called it, to hide her disquiet that each of her three children were tarred with the same brush.

"Portia had Titian hair, you know," she told us.

There didn't seem any point in telling her that Shakespeare held no sway with my peers.

The talk that morning centred around Deathwish, another recently formed garage band who were now on the cusp of disbanding. Some question-mark over the musical allegiance of the drummer in whose bedroom a Phil Collins album had recently been discovered: *Against All Odds*.

"Jesus," said Elly, who knew about my copy of that exact album but would carry my dark secret to her grave, if it came to it.

At the window, something caught my eye.

Not something.

Someone.

He stood at the end of the small, rickety pier, gazing out to sea. Not in a dreamy way, as I was wont to do. But with purpose. Focus. Looking for something that he would surely find, with a glare of such intensity. He wore skinny jeans. We called them *tight* back then. Milky blue jeans with the accidental-on-purpose rips along the thighs and across the knees.

A green parka with the hint of a Walkman poking out of a pocket, and of course, a pair of Doc Martens, scruffy enough to suggest he'd driven his father's car over them a few times. A shock of black curly hair. Brown eyes. Skin that wasn't tanned but looked like it could, given a chance.

He turned then and the sun poured over his face and down his body and he seemed otherworldly somehow. Ethereal. I drank him in like a Rock Shandy. He was the Heathcliff to my Cathy, I decided. The Mork to my Mindy. The flake in my 99. He waved and I waved back before I realised that he was waving at someone else and I lowered my hand slowly so no one would notice.

"I'm in love," I told Elly on the way home for dinner. I was in no hurry because, for starters, my sudden outbreak of love was proving incompatible with haste and also, it was Tuesday, which meant pork chops and boiled potatoes and mashed turnips with brown sauce with a glass of milk on the side and two biscuits – one fancy, one plain – for dessert. Elly's dinners were more exotic. Her mother made curry with raisins in it. I told my mother about the raisins once and she wouldn't believe me.

"Brilliant," said Elly who was in love herself and eager for some company in the endeavour. "Who is he?"

When I told her, her face darkened with worry. "He's . . . very popular," she said.

"Out of my league, you mean."

"No way! Just . . . you know. Tricky to gain access."

I nodded. I knew how precarious our position was, out here on the periphery.

"I can't help who I fall in love with, can I?" I said. The drama was powerful. I could feel the pull of it already. Epic it was. Like a battle. And there I was, a casualty already. A fallen soldier. A prisoner of war.

She nodded, grim. She understood. We linked arms and made plans to visit O'Connor Jeans again that Saturday to try on the Levi's we'd been saving for. We'd been trying the same pair on for months and were about three weeks' pocket-money away from the prize. With jeans like those . . . well, anything was possible, we agreed.

The making of this plan took us all along the estuary, to the end of our road where the smell of furious turnip reached for us like the steam that rises from a cow pat on a hot afternoon.

We stopped outside Elly's house. "What are you having for dinner?" I asked, briefly distracted from my situation.

She shrugged. "Pasta bake, I think."

My mouth watered. I'd mentioned pasta to my mother several weeks ago but she'd just said, "Mmmm" and continued poking the charred remains of a cod across a blackened frying pan.

"I'll ring you later," Elly said. "We can come up with more plans."

I loved that. We. I wasn't alone. I had back-up.

Being in love turned out to be a fairly full-time occupation. First of all, there were the imagined scenarios in my head which were time-consuming to set up. The walking. The talking. The handholding. The clinches.

Oh, the clinches. They could stop me in mid-sentence, mid-*EastEnders*, mid-walk-to-the-shops-for-a-sliced-pan.

"Those dishes will be dry before you get that tea-towel anywhere near them, my girl," my mother said, grabbing the towel from my hands and flicking a corner of it against my bare leg. A good aim, she had. And a deft wrist.

"*Ciara has a great imagination*," my English teacher wrote in my school report. Turns out she was right. The clinches. I had been reading a lot of Jilly Cooper and Sidney Sheldon which helped fuel my imaginings.

Then there was the strategic positioning. A complicated system of finding out where he'd be at various hours of the day and night and then strolling oh-so-casually into that very place at that very time. Standing at the pinball machine with Elly placed in pole position, all the better to see him, my dear.

"Where is he?" Hissed through a tiny gap at the corner of my mouth. Another ball down the chute. Another life lost.

"He's at four o'clock," she said, glancing around under cover of a toss of her long brown hair and bleached fringe. Magnificent, she was.

"What's he wearing?"

"What he always wears."

"Who's he with?"

"There's a gang of them."

"Any girls?"

"Yeah."

"How many?"

I could see Elly doing a brief headcount while pretending to count the change in her purse to see if she had enough money, for a milkshake perhaps. Cunning.

"Three. No wait, four. One of them's shaved her head."

Talking about it. That was probably the most time-consuming bit. Hours we spent, against a backdrop of *Brothers in Arms* ("So Far Away from Me"*) talking, talking, talking.

In the end, all we really came up with were these two facts:

I loved a boy.

The boy didn't love me back. Nor was he aware of my existence, as far as we could make out.

So far, despite our great efforts, I had managed to detain him in conversation on only one occasion. He was waiting for a bus and I "happened" along. Here's how it went:

Him: Hiya, Claire.

Me: Um, it's actually . . .

Him: Do you have the time?

Me (coquettish): For what?

Him (talking in slow, loud voice): Do. You. Know. What. Time. It. Is? (pointing to his wrist to further clarify)

Me: Oh, eh, yes, of course, it's . . . (pushing the sleeve of my – matching – parka up my arm) Oh, no, sorry, I've . . . forgotten my watch.

Bus arrives and I disappear in a dark cloud of exhaust fumes.

Him (hopping on bus, graceful as a gazelle): Seeya, Claire.

That was it. So far. In my darkest moments I conceded that it wasn't a lot.

I came up with the plan on a wet Wednesday afternoon, slumped in front of *Monsters of Rock* on the telly.

A love letter.

Why hadn't I thought of it before?

"Are you sure that will work?" Elly asked.

"Positive."

"What are you going to write?"

"Something discreet. But clever. Original. And intriguing."

If my plan was to work, I would have to be outed as the author so there was no way I wanted to claim responsibility for a lengthy tome where sense was far outweighed by sensibility.

No.

Like many stories I've written, a couple of things happened to trigger the piece.

The first thing was The Scorpions. I was doing some fairly obsessive listening to "Still Loving You" around this time, the needle digging a deep furrow into that particular groove of the record.

The second thing was my mother, shaking her head at the kitchen table, leaning over my book list. "Shocking," she said. "The price of that Spanish book. And it's a new edition, of course, so no chance of getting it second hand."

Spanish! Of course! The guttural sound of it, the dance of the words along a sentence, the V's pronounced as B's, the speed of it, the shape of the words in your mouth, the comic strangeness of the upside-down punctuation marks.

It was perfect.

I kissed my mother's cheek and she glanced up, still annoyed at the shocking price of schoolbooks and the sneakiness of the new editions that parted her from her hard-earned cash, but now confused at my sudden display of affection.

"Thanks, Mam."

"What for?"

"Everything."

She regarded me with deep suspicion as I left the kitchen at a trot.

Still Loving You.

That's what I'd write.

But – and here was the rub, as Shakespeare might say – I'd write it *in Spanish*. How intriguing could a Titian-haired girl with gym knickers and a jolly-hockey-stick be?

I wrote it on my hand.

Te quiero todavia.

A lot of time was spent on the type of paper I should use. Nothing flowery or flouncy. Nothing *love-lettery*. No pictures of butterflies or any other insect. And absolutely no hearts.

In the end, I bought plain but expensive writing paper that was neither white nor cream but something in the middle. Ivory, the lady in the shop called it. I measured the length and the breadth of a page and plotted where each word should begin and end, so that the sentence would be perfectly central and in proportion to the rest of the page.

I wrote each of the three words with lavish strokes and flourishes the likes of which I had never achieved before or indeed since.

Te Quiero Todavia.

No "from".

No "to".

Just three words. In Spanish. Anonymous. Like a Valentine's Day card except a letter instead of a card and June instead of February.

Inspired.

I bought an envelope. A stamp. Folded the page oh-so-carefully. Slid it inside the envelope. Gummed it. Sealed it. Wrote his name in a careful disguise of block capitals on the front. Copied his address out of the phone book. All this took me less than twenty minutes. The standing in front of the post box, deliberating, took a good bit longer. In the end, Elly grabbed it, stuffed it through the dark mouth of the postbox.

"Whatcha do that for?" Incensed.

"It's nearly six. We'll be late for dinner if we stand here much longer."

"Fair enough." Our mothers were united in their love of punctuality.

"What are you having?"

"Gammon steak with pineapple." Nonchalant. Like it was nothing.

"Actual pineapple?"

"Tinned."

"Oh."

It was Friday so we were having grilled mackerel, with mam roaring, "Watch out for the bones, for the love of God!" before every mouthful.

Even the plate of smelly, greasy mackerel with its mean, hard bones couldn't quell my excitement, my nervousness, my anticipation as to what might happen . . .

In the end, nothing happened. Not really. There were rumours of course. There were always rumours. About a letter. An anonymous letter. A foreign language, people said. Italian maybe.

Nobody knew what it meant.

Or who had sent it.

Perhaps my chemistry teacher was right after all. Her comment in my school report read, "*More planning needed in the organisation and execution of experiments.*"

Never a truer word . . .

Ciara Geraghty lives in Dublin with three children, one husband and a dog. She has written four novels: *Saving Grace, Becoming Scarlett, Finding Mr. Flood* and *Lifesaving for Beginners*.

Unconditional Love

Caroline Grace-Cassidy

I close my eyes behind the open white hall door in Stella Gardens and listen to the seagulls squawk, their sounds combining, making interesting music in my young head. I'm immediately reminded of "Billie Jean". I hum it. I tap my white-runnered foot and watch the multicoloured laces bop. I'm totally and utterly in love with Michael Jackson and I know in my heart that someday I will marry him. Sometimes in interviews I know exactly what he's going to say before he says it. I get him.

I stop tapping and I move from behind the door to the gap where I feel the cool outdoor air on my face. I open my eyes ever so slowly and gaze up as the seagulls' whiteness soars across my head and they dip in and around the flats. I move out as my eyes follow them twisting and turning my body like this until I become slightly dizzy and only then do I stop. I'm reminded of the Waltzers in Funderland. My favourite.

I leave the door ajar as is my granny's wish and I smell the Brasso from the newly scrubbed metallic numbers on the hall door: 141. The knocker and gold letterbox gleam at me. I step over the newly disinfected step and hop onto the little path as I reach for the gate. Maybe it's because I don't have a gate on my own detached house in the suburbs that this gate holds such immense excitement for me. I love how it creaks when I open it, like my dad's guitar case. I love lifting the latch and replacing it. My very own fortress. I inhale the air deeply and am instantly in my happy safe place.

I'm on a journey. I never take this journey at home. I am not allowed. I am going to the shops on my own. I am going for the messages. I have the five-pound note in the sole of my runner. Under my knee-high white socks. There is a picture at the top of my socks but it's faded so much now I can't remember what it was. I crumple my toes up tight in my runners. Five pounds is a fortune to be trusted with. I am getting a small turnover of bread, four slices of hard cheese and two hard tomatoes. She always emphasises the word *hard*.

The house next door is so close the two front doors are almost touching. I really like Mrs Nolan – if she sees me skip past she will ask me in for a glass of TK red lemonade. It's always warm but I don't mind. I love her ornaments – especially the small brass man with the fishing rod. Her blind is still down. I skip on. Rita Nolan (lots of Nolans around here) shuffles down the road towards me in her slippers (no one wears their slippers outside in my area).

"I only wear them in the mornin', love, to get me bottle of milk," she told me the time I enquired. "Me feet are swelled in the mornin'." Her slippers don't fit quite right so her heels stand on the backs of them, squashing the brown material down. Sometimes when she walks I can see that she's not really wearing tights at all but socks that look like tights but only come up to her knee. "Knee highs," my mother explained.

"Howrya, love?" she asks me now. No one ever asks me how I am on the street at home. "Howsa yer granny? Is her ulster any better?"

Granny has a pretty bad leg ulcer.

"Not too bad, thanks." I like playing chatting on the street – it makes me feel older and I fold my arms up high the same way Rita has hers. "She's going to see Professor Higgins in the morning." I divulge as much information as I can because I know this is what Rita likes.

"Tell her I'll call in later for her Christmas Club money," she says and off she shuffles only about four steps before she begins another stop and chat with Michael the window cleaner. I stand with my arms still folded. He balances a ladder and a red bucket on his old-fashioned black bicycle. He removes his cap when he talks to her. I want to stay and listen but I know I'd better move on. I bet they're talking about the fall Mrs Hughes had in Number 76. It was a bad one from what I'd overheard. Stood up to feed the gas meter and keeled over. On the floor all night, poor love. Till the home help knocked at seven with her porridge and couldn't get an answer. A broken hip by all accounts. That son of hers in London has a lot to answer for. The louser.

I turn the corner and head for the lane (the lane is the shortest way) – all in all it usually takes four minutes to get to the shop. I know this because Granny bought me a digital watch from the stall on O'Connell Bridge. It is pink with a plastic strap and I absolutely love it.

I stop for a minute and stand looking in the window of Lily Bon-Bon's sweet shop. I will come back later for my quarter of apple drops. I made up my mind in bed last night, under the many woolly blankets and the pink, blue and yellow stripy cotton sheets, snuggled into my granny's back, that I'd go for apple drops. I have just been too focused on strawberry sherbets for ages now and it's time for a change. Granny likes mint Toffos. She keeps hers in the pocket of her apron and can peel the paper off without having to look at them.

I pull myself away from the window display of red-and-white candy canes and I push the heavy door into Tom's shop. There is always sawdust on the floor. Tom is the biggest man I have ever seen in my life. That's because he's from Kerry, my granny told me. I'm never going to Kerry – the people are just too big. I stand on my tippy-toes and shout my order.

"Two slices of hard cheese when yer ready, Tom, please!"

Tom may be big but he's slightly deaf so you have to shout.

He smiles at me in his long light-brown coat and I see his two missing teeth.

"Comin' up, missy!" he roars at me and my fringe blows on his breath.

His gigantic hands lift the largest block of cheese in the world (from Kerry too, I imagine) and he slices.

I'm not sure I like the smell in here – sometimes I do and sometimes I don't. I turn and find the cardboard box with the tomatoes. There is an old man feeling them so I stand patiently behind him. He makes a growling sort of noise as he rummages and rummages and then he chooses one. It takes him ages to straighten up and he has to hold onto his back. I smile at him and I bend down. It's not an easy job. 'Hard' seems easy enough to figure out but, you see, they *all* seem hard to me. But they can't all be hard otherwise that man wouldn't have felt so many. It's very tough. I dig right to the back and pick out two perfectly red, rounded, hard tomatoes. Then I pull off my runner and sock and get my money. I pay big Tom.

I skip back through the lane and in through the door. Granny's in the tiny kitchen. Enough room for one person only. The table is set. The tea's being made. I hand over the merchandise and her change. She smiles at me. She feels and smells and pokes and prods and I might have done alright because she doesn't say "What ails that man at all, selling this rubbish? Does he think I came down in the last shower?"

I pull out my wooden chair and she butters the fresh turnover and makes up our cheese and tomato sandwiches. She always makes my one first. We are going into town on the No. 3 bus after this and I'm sure she will buy me that Michael Jackson poster I saw on Henry Street. She'll defo buy me an éclair. She wants to get her fruit and veg in Moore Street. When she's done the dishes she will look into the glass above the fireplace, brush her dark curly perm with her red comb and push on her glasses. She never wears make-up or puts in her good teeth unless we are going out at night-time. I much prefer her without her teeth.

I often wonder why she spends so much time with me: she has

loads of grandchildren, but deep down I think it's because she loves me the best and I love her the best too. I always sleep the night with her at weekends. She has to live on her own, you see, on account of Lar (that was her husband) being dead. I worry about her every minute I'm not with her and sometimes I put my head under my pillow at home and sob myself to sleep when I think of her on her own all night in the house. I don't want her to be lonely. She's too nice. I don't want her to meet a new husband or anything like that but I would love her to live with us. She can't, she tells me, and that's that. She's really kind to everyone, she feeds the birds every single morning and night and she takes such great care of her Geranium flowers. They have to come in from the tiny garden every night and she puts them on the stairs.

I eat my sandwich and we don't need to talk.

She's dead now. I'm old. Well, oldish. I'm thirty-six. I wasn't there when she died. I so wanted to be. I wanted to be with her so, so badly when she was leaving me. I never wanted her to be alone. She'd never have let me die alone, I know that much. I asked them was she in any immediate danger when I left and they said no. I shouldn't have gone. I should have stayed there 24/7 but I didn't. She would have. They aren't God, my mother told me. I wasn't a bit afraid of watching her die, I always saw myself there holding her blue-veined hand and whispering comforting things into her oh-so-familiar face.

Regret.

When I pull up my childhood in my head these are the thoughts I am filled with: her warmth, strength, kindness, loyalty, defiance, independence; pink balloons, pigs' feet, sweeping carpets, open fire, 'chucky' eggs; Gay Byrne on the old wireless and the smell of Brasso wafting up the stairs. When she went all modern and got the electric fire, I'd hold the knife through the grids with bread on the end making toast. Toast has never tasted so good.

She was my wonderful granny, Margaret Kilroy. She was as strong a woman as there can be and a true fighter in every sense of the word. So incredibly strong. I miss her every single day and there are always times when I just want to have a cuppa with her and a hard cheese and tomato sandwich but I can't. I do talk to her in my own way a lot and that helps. Such memories need to be cherished and respected and never forgotten. She gave me unconditional love and I was so lucky to have such a woman in my life.

I called my baby Maggie after her – I know she'd have loved that.

Caroline Grace-Cassidy trained at the Gaiety School of Acting before landing her first television role as Mary Mull on the BAFTA-winning children's programme *Custer's Last Stand-Up*. She then went on to appear in various productions for BBC/RTÉ/TG4 and TV3 and various feature films. She is a founding member and a creative director of Smart Blondes Productions. Their debut film premiered at the Galway Film Fleadh in 2013 and they are currently in production on their second film. She is also a regular panellist on *Midday* for TV3. In 2011 she was delighted to secure a three-book deal with Poolbeg Press. Her debut novel *When Love Takes Over* was released in February 2012 and her second novel *The Other Side of Wonderful* hit shelves in June 2013. For more information, see www.carolinegracecassidy.com.

If All Else Fails, Blame the Dog

Niamh Greene

On the wall in my kitchen there hangs a vintage chart on "moral training" that I bought a few years ago at an auction. Based on the rules of the Children's National Guild of Courtesy of 1898, it succinctly outlines the mannerly code of conduct that youngsters aspired to at the time. Funnily enough, the guidelines are still very relevant today. In fact, as I often remind my own children, they provide the perfect blueprint for the sort of saintly life your mother would be proud of.

If only I'd had them to refer to when I was a child myself . . .

Be honest, truthful and pure:
Regardless of the circumstances, honesty is always the best policy. Unless of course you happen to accidentally break a precious family heirloom / destroy your sister's favourite top / get caught breaking a curfew. Then forget about telling the truth and blame the dog for everything.

Do not use bad language:
Believe me, you do not want to be caught saying the f-word on the street by your mother because the disappointed look on

her face will haunt you for the rest of your days. Cursing is a hard habit to break, so why start? Ditto smoking, drinking and kissing unsuitable boys.

Help your parents as much as you can and do your best to please them:

Violently slamming doors, making empty threats to run away and howling "I didn't ask to be born!" multiple times a day do not count as pleasing behaviours. Right now, you're convinced that your parents know nothing, but the day will come when you realise that, incredibly, they were right about pretty much everything. Usually this light-bulb moment coincides with the happy day you have children of your own. That's called karma, my friend.

Be kind to your brothers and sisters. Do not be selfish but share all your good things:

Siblings are not the enemy. It's hard to see this when everything they do seems specially designed to aggravate you, but it's true. In time you'll grow up and you'll actually be able to have a conversation without wanting to throttle one another. Difficult as it is to imagine, you'll genuinely like each other and quarrels about crossing the invisible line you've drawn on the back seat of the car so you don't have to touch each other on journeys will seem silly. Instead, you'll sit down to eat together because you want to – crazy concept, I know. You'll even look back on your childhood and laugh. Until of course the whole "You lost my signed Nirvana T-shirt" debacle raises its ugly head. Then all bets are off and you revert back to acting like your teenage selves in a heartbeat.

Be respectful to your teachers. Their work is very difficult and trying:

You might think that you have the bum deal at school – after all, you're the one who has to learn obscure Irish verbs and memorise useless French grammar. However, when you grow up, you will realise that teachers may not actually have the life of Riley that you thought they did. Why do you think your parents are so glad to drop you off at the school gates every morning? They need a rest, that's why.

Do not make slides on the pavement or throw orange peel there:

Now, I love throwing orange peel as much as the next person, but your mother is right – this type of illicit activity might be all fun and games initially, but it'll end in tears. Ditto running with scissors, incessantly ringing neighbours' doorbells for the *craic*, and sticking Lego up your nose.

Do not speak or drink with food in your mouth:

This is only cute when you're a toddler. Do you want people to have to duck when you eat? No, I didn't think so.

Remember to say "please" and "thank you":

It only takes a second, but it makes a big difference. People respond well to courteous behaviour so start practising early and you'll be extremely popular. It may also help you to avoid unpleasant road-rage incidents and run-ins with the law in later life.

Mind your own business:

Gossiping about others can be fun, but ultimately it's not big and it's not clever. Would you like it if people were sniping about you behind your back? No nasty texting, tweeting or Facebooking either please.

I'd also add a few of my own, more modern, rules to the list.

Dream big:

You can achieve anything you set your mind to. All you need to do is work hard and focus. When I was a child, I dreamed of being a writer one day. I still pinch myself when I see my novels on shelves.

Don't stop believing:

Yes, this might be just a corny song to you, but the sentiment is real. Keep dreaming, don't give up, it's never too late. It took me a while – and quite a few wrong turns – to get where I am now, but I made it in the end. Besides, nothing is ever a waste – it's all experience. (Or, in my case, material for stories.)

Accept your hair / body shape / wonky nose:

Why waste time worrying? You are perfect just the way you

are. Learn to love yourself early on in life and save yourself a bucket-load of unnecessary angst and heartbreak. As writer Nora Ephron once said: "I wish I had worn a bikini every day when I was 26." You will inevitably curse yourself for not capitalising on your youthful beauty, so put the bikini on today, even if only metaphorically.

Appreciate your youth:

They say that youth is wasted on the young – it's only when you're old and grey that you realise you had it so good. My top tip? Enjoy it while you can. Wring every day of its last drop. Before you know it, you'll be looking back, not quite believing that you are officially "all grown up". Supposedly.

Niamh Greene is a novelist and columnist with the *Evening Herald*. Her latest novel, *Coco's Secret*, is published by Penguin. Find her on Twitter @niamh_greene and Facebook at niamhgreenebooks.

Whispered Words of Wisdom

Carmel Harrington

If I was a child again . . .

What a scary thought! Would I choose to go back and do it all over again if I were given the opportunity? I don't think I would have the energy! But if I could go back for just a short visit, I would choose to go back to a time when I was a young teenage girl, on the brink of that often difficult transition from child to young woman. At fourteen years old I was terribly self-conscious and had far too many worries that were ill-warranted. I often think of the wasted time I spent as a young girl fretting about how I looked. Peer pressure came from all sorts of places, but the worst pressure came from myself. Wouldn't it be wonderful to be able to go back and change that? To take away that overwhelming feeling of not fitting in and being different and teach myself to look those self-critical demons squarely in the eye whenever I looked at my reflection?

If I could, here's what I would whisper repeatedly to myself until I believed it to be true: "You are perfect exactly as you are. You are not too tall or too skinny – you are simply a beautiful young girl with a wonderful future ahead of her."

I would then repeat several times: "And despite that moron

who called you a boy recently, you do *not* look like a boy!"

Actually, I can still remember that moment nearly thirty years later. It was a moment that I would say most who were present at the time would not even remember, because really it wasn't such a big deal. But back then it felt like a big deal and I've never forgotten it, the memory never dulling with time. This particular memory is one where a neighbour mistook me for my brother, loudly saying it in front of a large group. Okay, I was tall and, yes, I had short hair, but come on – I was a girl! Clearly he should have gone to Specsavers!

I remember that flush of embarrassment in the realisation that I had been mistaken for a boy – not for the first time either. My mortification only intensified as I heard giggles from those around me. I bravely smiled and pretended that it didn't bother me. But it did bother me; in fact, it bothered me deeply. I cried myself to sleep that night, hating how I looked and wishing with all my might that fairy tales did exist and my Fairy Godmother would suddenly appear any minute. I knew exactly what I would wish for too: about five inches chopped off my gangly frame.

And that makes me so very sad. To think that I would have chosen to change how I look had I got the opportunity is undeniably sad. If I look at photographs of myself back then, do you know what I see now? I can see a young, pretty girl with big blue eyes and an even bigger mop of curly dark hair. I looked absolutely fine back then, but of course how you actually look and how you perceive you look are two very different things to any young person with insecurities.

So what would I teach myself if I could go back in time? I would teach myself that in this wondrous world we live in, this diversely imperfect world, it is in fact our very differences that make it so gloriously interesting. Whether we are tall, short, fat, thin, curly or straight-haired, red, brunette or blonde, we are all perfect just as we are.

How would I impart this wisdom? Wouldn't it be amazing if I could put pen to paper and write a letter to my younger self? What if I could simply stroll to the local post office and pop a letter into a post-box marked *Time Travel* and *whoosh*, off it goes!

Here is what I would say in that letter.

Dear Carmel,

Now this is going to sound a little bit crazy, but remember that movie you watched with Fiona, Shelley and John last week that had that very cute guy Michael J Fox in it? It was called Back to the Future *and you had never seen anything like that before! Well, you might want to sit down for a second because, albeit without the help of any vintage DeLorean cars or mad scientists who answer to the name of Doc, this letter you have just received has in fact been sent all the way back from 2013.*

That sounds like a lifetime away, I know, and truth be told it is a lifetime away. You have so many wonderful adventures to experience, and the places you will travel to between your now and my now will blow your mind. I'm smiling just thinking about the fun that's ahead of you! I know you must be wondering who is reaching out to you nearly three decades later and for what purpose? Well, let me introduce myself first of all: my name is Carmel Harrington. How can I put this without freaking out your fourteen-year-old mind? Okay, brace yourself, because this is Back to the Future *territory. This letter is from you! Well, an older version of you as I'm now forty-two years old. I'll give you a moment to let that sink in!*

I'm trying to work out what questions you would have for me if I were actually sitting in front of you and I reckon you want to know about boys. Am I right? Yep! Thought so! So, yes, you will love and you will be loved and that guy you have a crush on? Well, he likes you too.

But I'm not here to talk about crushes, Carmel pet. I have lots I need to share with you. First, stop twisting your hair. You are doing that right now, aren't you? You always do that when you're nervous. That's a habit I still haven't managed to shift. I'll keep working on that one! There's nothing to be nervous about, though, as I'm just here to help. I promise.

I want to talk to you about how you look, or rather how you think you look! You are fourteen years old right now and I know that you are very self-conscious, about your height in particular. You have always been the tallest girl in the class and you hate having that particular tag, as you are also very shy. You try so hard to fade into the background, but that's a bit of a tall order (sorry, terrible pun I know!).

Let's see if I can reassure you about something first of all. I know that late at night, when you can't sleep, that extremely over-active imagination of yours goes wild and you often fret that you will continue to grow and grow until one day you are over seven feet tall. You have already imagined the national headlines: Wexford Giant in Guinness Book of Records.

Relax – you have pretty much stopped growing now. You will reach the dizzying heights of five foot ten by the time you are fifteen and then that's pretty much it. Relieved? Good!

I know that right now it feels like you will always be this lanky, skinny girl who gets mistaken for a boy far too often. Here's a little bit of free advice from your older and wiser self: the short hair doesn't help, pet, so maybe let it grow again. And trust me when I say that pretty soon it will be impossible that you will be mistaken for a boy. Change is afoot. Or abreast so to speak! Ahem!

I also know that there are nights that you cry yourself to sleep because you are so self-conscious and feel so different to all the other seemingly perfect, petite girls in your class. Why is it that you never tell anyone how you feel? You have always bottled up all your insecurities inside, with the occasional confession in your journal. Carmel, it's not a sign of weakness to share with others how you feel. It is, in fact, a sign of great strength. Don't be afraid to let others in.

Here's the thing, pet, you are wasting far too much time worrying about something that you have no control over (you can't change genetics). More importantly, you have no need to worry about your height. You are beautiful, just as you are. I'll say that again, because I know that you have thrown your eyes up to the heavens in immediate disbelief when you read that sentence.

You are beautiful, just as you are.

Here's the thing, did you know that you are not the only girl who hates putting on her gym gear in the communal changing rooms? In that room that makes you break out in hives every time you go into it, nearly everyone else has a hang-up about how they look too. They believe themselves to be too short, too fat, too thin, too ugly or too tall. It is unlikely that anyone in the group thinks that they are perfect.

I'd love to visit that locker room and ask all of your friends and classmates to sit down in a circle, facing each other. I would then ask everyone there to be brutally honest and to place in the centre of the circle all of their own particular insecurities about how they look. And I reckon that you and your classmates would be completely shell-shocked to hear how many of you are plagued with self-doubt.

And listen to this, as it's going to make your head spin. Do you know that many of those same girls you have envied for years, those girls with the lovely curves and petite frames, in turn envy you? The girls with beautiful curves feel that they are too fat and look at your skinny frame and wish they could be the same. And the small girls, that you think are so perfectly pint-sized, in turn wish they were as tall as you as they are fed up being thought of as much younger than they actually are. Crazy, huh? I know you don't believe me, but I know this to be true. How do I know? Well, I'm still friends with some of your classmates now. Like me, they are now older and wiser and they have shared with me how they felt as teenagers.

So my point is, Carmel, everyone has a different definition of what they think is perfect. It's tough being fourteen years old and much easier to think there is something wrong with you than right with you but, honestly, you are going to be just fine. All five foot ten of you!

Do me a favour though – please try to stop worrying about

what everyone else thinks about you and start believing in you.

Yes, you are tall. Facts are facts and you will continue to be among the tallest of the girls in your circle throughout your life. Is that such a bad thing though? Think about it for a second: isn't it kind of wonderful to be tall?

As you get older and make your way around the world, you will soon see that height loses its significance very quickly. What's far more important is being a good person, a kind person, someone who can make a difference to others and the world. So shoulders back, stand up proud and straight, and work on being the very best version of you that you can possibly be.

Remember, you are beautiful just as you are.
Keep dreaming (and writing!)
Lots of love,
Carmel x

Carmel Harrington is the bestselling author of the award-winning eBook *Beyond Grace's Rainbow*, published by the HarperCollins digital imprint, HarperImpulse. She is also a popular freelance writer and a regular contributor to a number of magazines. She also loves playwriting and her first play *A Dunganstown Romance* was staged in 2013 by the New Line Theatre. Her second novel *Sleep of Dreams* is now completed and will be published later this year and she is currently working on a sequel to *Beyond Grace's Rainbow*. Married to Roger with two small children Amelia and Nate, she lives in Wexford, Ireland, where life is pretty idyllic, full of stories, songs, hide-and-seek, Mickey Mouse, walks on the beach, tickles, kisses, chocolate treats and most of all love. For more information please find her at www.carmelharrington.com.

Memories

Andrea Hayes

As I sat in my back garden reading a book in the shade, I heard something rare and exciting, something I suddenly realised I had never actually heard since I moved into our house: the sound of those chimes, once a familiar sound on the avenue in Dublin where I had spent so many happy summers as a child. Suddenly joyous memories of my childhood came flooding back. I felt that giddy feeling inside again, knowing that the tinkle of the traditional ice-cream van signalled a treat on the way, the magical unmistakable sound announcing ice cream!

It was still thrilling. I closed my eyes and allowed that quintessential sound of summer to bring me back to a wonderful time in my life. Suddenly I found myself thinking: I miss those long hot summer days when I had nothing to do but laze around, playing hopscotch, kick the can, hanging out, just playing and having fun with my friends . . . no responsibilities, no problems, no worries.

Then from nowhere I heard a big booming voice announce: "Do you, Andrea Hayes, hereby officially tender your resignation as an adult and accept the responsibility of a nine-year-old?"

"I do."

"The terms of your contract are as follows:

You will have to spend hours doing nothing but building with Lego blocks. You will laugh, play, agree to be carefree and live in the moment. You will love getting up early on a Saturday morning to watch cartoons. You will want to be She-Ra (Princess of Power!). You will ask your parents about changing your name to that of your favourite cartoon character, Jem, because she's in a band and, more importantly, She's Truly Outrageous. You will believe your childhood friends will never leave your side because you exchanged handmade friendship bracelets. Your friends with friendship bracelets will be part of your secret club and you will all want to be Goonies. You will think that soggy sand-filled sandwiches and lemonade at the beach is better than the food in any gourmet restaurant. You will spend hours searching the garden for ladybirds, insects, bugs and bees. You will think that Smarties are better than money because you can eat them. You will want to spend hours rehearsing your "made-up" shows and plays with your friends on hot summer days so you can put on a final performance for your family and neighbours. You will accept that life is simple: multiplication tables will be the only stressful part of your day.

You must agree to believe that the world is fair. That everyone is honest and good. You must believe in fairy tales and happy-ever-afters and trust that dreams do come true and anything is possible. You must believe in the power of smiles, hugs, and a kiss to make things better. You must believe that putting out your tongue will prove if you are or aren't telling the truth! You must trust and believe in the power of imagination, making tents from blankets, knitting socks, making jewellery boxes with matchsticks, necklaces with beads, and making angels in the snow and sand.

Finally, if you are officially stepping down from adulthood, then close your eyes and count to 10 . . ."

1 – 2 – 3 – 4 – 5 – 6 – 7 – 8 – 9 – 10!

Then I heard my brother's voice calling, "*Ready or not, here I come!*"

I opened my eyes and realised we must be playing hide-and-seek. I was behind the couch in the living room. Instinct kicked in and I started to climb onto the top of the couch, then jumped from the couch to the armchair, blissfully unaware of any potential danger. I heard my brother shouting my name, then suddenly I was shouting, "*Na-na-na-na-naaaa! You can't catch me!*" I jumped again to the dining-room table – this time I wasn't so lucky as I lost balance and slipped and found myself on the ground.

Before I had time to cry, I heard . . . "*Tag! You're it!*"

"No, that's not fair!" I said, and then I heard my mother's voice reminding me that I had a big day tomorrow.

Suddenly I remembered what tomorrow would bring and joy spread through every inch of my body. Tomorrow was my birthday, and this was a *big* birthday. I could not wait to be ten years old. For weeks I had thought about how great it must be to have double digits. A milestone in the life of any little girl. *Ten.* I don't know why I imagined that everything would be different if I was a decade old but definitely my birthday could not come soon enough for me. Only one night's sleep separated me from finally being *big*, finally ten years old. Excitement, anticipation, and joy filled my heart.

I went to bed with a sense of wonder and expectation. I sat in front of my window and looked out. It was already dark outside and I waited impatiently for something special: I was waiting for the first star to appear in the sky so I could make a special wish, just in time for my birthday. I looked impatiently at the black sky.

Time passed and my disappointment grew as I still hadn't spotted a star.

"I can't go to bed yet! There are still no stars, Daddy!" I muttered as I sadly looked at my dad, as if he were to blame for the fact that not a single star had found its way to earth.

"You must have a little patience," he said. "Your star is a very special star – it's a special dream star. When you dream tonight you can dream for whatever you want and your special dream star will make all your wishes come true, just in time for your birthday."

This sounded very promising. But I wondered what would happen if I didn't see the star in my dreams.

I jumped into my bed and waited for my dad to tuck me in. Then, like every night, he told me a story. But on this evening the fantasy world that my father conjured up with his words was very exciting, a world where dreams come true and anything is possible, especially if you had a special birthday dream star that was sent to boys and girls on the eve of their tenth birthday. I tried again and again to look out my window through a narrow slit in the curtains, to see if finally a single star would appear. My dad reassured me that all I needed to do was sleep and when I woke up I would be ten and all my dreams would come true.

I drifted off to sleep and then I flew high into the clouds. I felt weightless as I twirled and tumbled through the sky, then suddenly I stopped at a bike shop and I could see the most beautiful shining red bike, with a beautiful basket and a shiny silver bell. I thought I would love that bike if I was big, and just as I had the thought the bike seemed to follow me, flying in the sky. I decided to jump on my new red bike and as I cycled I beeped my shiny silver bell so the clouds would disappear to let me through. Every time I rang the bell I found myself somewhere new. I stopped at Nana and Granda's where they had a big brightly wrapped present for me. I opened it and smiled from ear to ear as I held my birthday present in my hands. I knew immediately what it was – inside the plastic bright-green cabbage, I knew I would have my very own Cabbage Patch Kid! How thrilling! Then my silver bell rang again and this time I was shopping with my big sisters and we were picking out a fancy new dress for my party with matching sparkly new shoes. I felt really special and big now – I knew I had grown as I needed to choose a size for ten-year-olds! There were more places to go as we needed to buy party treats and decorations so I set off on my bike with my sisters beside me. Everyone seemed to know it was my birthday and before long my basket was filled with goodies. I rang my bell for a final time and suddenly I was in the cake shop looking at a big, pretty, round cake with pink frosting and

I could read the writing. It said: *Happy 10th Birthday, Andrea*. I was twirling around and around, giddy with excitement. All my dreams really had come true.

Then I woke up to the sound of all my family singing "Happy Birthday". I was still a little tired but finally the big day had arrived . . .

"Close your eyes, Andrea, and count to ten . . ."

1 – 2 – 3 – 4 – 5 – 6 – 7 – 8 – 9 – 10!

I opened my eyes and I could hear the magical sound of the ice-cream van. As the chime drifted into the distance I was reminded never to stop wishing on stars because dreams really do come true.

A well-known face and voice in the world of television and radio in Ireland, Andrea is best known for presenting TV3's hugely successful series *Ireland's Animal A&E* which recently aired on Channel 5 in the UK and on a number of other channels worldwide, including the Discovery Channel across Europe. She also presented *Dublin Airport: Life Stories* on TV3, a six-part TV3 series following the broad range of stories which are part of daily life at Dublin Airport. She is a regular on the sofa on *Ireland AM* and has hosted *Midday* on many occasions. She has been working for TV3 since 2005. Her voice is familiar to the TV3 audience as she has been the voice of the station for the last eight years. In addition to her work with TV3, Andrea keeps busy with radio and voice-over work. She has been working for Dublin's Sunshine 106.8 since 2009, and currently presents a talk show called *Saturday Live* on Saturdays. She is well-known on the hosting circuit and recently hosted The Wedding Fair at the RDS. She also enjoys writing and has written articles for *Woman's Way*, *Oh Baby* magazine and *The Waiting Room* magazine.

One More Day

Emma Heatherington

If I was a child again, I would ask God for one more day with her. Just one day to warn us, one day to say goodbye.

The day in question will live with me forever, even though it was spelt out in death in an ill-prepared, no-nonsense, no-time-for-digesting-what-was-going-on way – and no time for an innocent mind to interpret why it was to happen. I still can't . . .

My mother Geraldine was the life and soul the party, the life and soul of our lives and of everyone who was lucky enough to know her.

I remember her taste in music. She was an accomplished singer and was into everyone from James Taylor to Leonard Cohen to The Police. She even liked Barry Manilow, much to my teenage disgust.

I remember the day she recognised my love for music. When I wrote my first musical aged only twelve, I remember how she advised me on structure and story, how she talked to me and helped me choose the right songs. She let me stay off school one day because she knew how much I loved one band in particular and didn't want to miss them on *Pebble Mill at One*. (Video recorders? I didn't trust those for one second and she knew it!)

I remember her smell, I remember her voice as she spoke as well as sang, but most of all I remember her laughter, and she laughed a lot.

I remember how she loved Levi's jeans, the discovery of MTV and Elton John's "I Guess That's Why They Call It the Blues", the angst of Angie in *EastEnders*, the way she would chuckle at John Cleese in *Fawlty Towers* and how she looked forward to a night out on the weekends when she could find a baby-sitter to look after us all.

She had a laugh that could stay in your heart forever and a smile with the most perfect white teeth I ever did see. She was proud, fiercely proud, and loyal beyond belief. If you were her child, her partner, her sister or her friend she loved you until the end. She adored her children and her family so much that she thought each and every person who came our way should adore them in equal measure. In fact, it's a lasting joke that if someone on the street admired one of us, she would make sure they complimented the other five individually, even if they couldn't tell one of us from another.

She had an ear for a tune, an eye for detail and good taste, a way with the written and spoken word and a humour that would light up a room no matter how many people were in it.

She was the baby of seven girls, was thought the world of by her sisters and was the apple of her father's eye. Photos show her as a petite, beautiful blonde standing with pride beside the tall, dark and handsome man she married.

We had moved into our new house a few months before it happened. We got the keys on a Wednesday night and she was so excited that she moved us into it in darkness, with no electricity, and lit the fire for light and warmth and we talked and sang through the night. She had colour schemes chosen for every room. She had plans for French windows, for a patio, for a place where the little ones could play. She had plans for everything.

I was fifteen years old when it happened. I had been out ten-pin bowling with friends the night before – a Friday – and just as I was leaving the house she asked me to wash up after our evening meal. I was in a rush to see my friends.

I said no.

Typical teenager, I guess, but nonetheless her words have stayed with me ever since.

"One day you will realise why I appreciate a bit of help," she told me as I slammed the door in full tantrum, which wasn't really true to my form. She wasn't angry, she barely raised her voice. She was just tired and weary of all the chores and daily necessities her life entailed.

I was the eldest – she was a thirty-six-year-old mum of six children in steps and stairs right down to the age of eight months. As a mum myself now, I can see clearly how the simple task of someone else washing-up would have meant so much to her.

I came home that night and peeped into her bedroom as she slept. The baby was in the cot, sleeping sound, her tiny hands laid back by her cheeks and the sound of her soft breathing made the house sound so peaceful.

I heard my father rise for work the next morning and then shortly afterwards I heard the baby cry and the sound of Mummy tending to her downstairs and then doing what all the experts told her: to go back to bed and sleep when the baby slept.

She asked for some help later that morning and again I was reluctant to expand from my own little world. I was tired, it was a Saturday, I had my own things to do. By eleven a.m., she was asking for the doctor, for her sisters, for anyone to relieve her of this strange pain that had overcome her. Indigestion, the doctor said, but he handed me a piece of paper with a phone number on it to call him in case things became worse.

My Aunt Eithna arrived and rubbed her back, telling her she would be okay and tried to soothe her younger sister as she writhed around the bed in pain, with no clue what was going on within her young body.

Another sister called and then panic set in. The doctor came

133

back, and then my ten-year-old brother ran to the end of the road and guided an ambulance to our new house.

We were in the sitting room, our new sitting room where she had lit that first fire only months before, kneeling in a circle and saying words of the Rosary with an elderly neighbour – words of religion that none of us were old enough to recognise.

My mummy died before 3 p.m. that Saturday, 4th May, 1991, just three weeks before her thirty-seventh birthday.

A massive heart attack, they said. There was no further explanation, really. The medics were as horrified as we were but no one as much as my dad who had returned from work at lunchtime to be met with such shock, such horror, that his young wife and the mother of his six children was gone. He had spoken to her that morning when he left for work as she stood with their baby girl in her arms, and when he returned from work she was gone.

She was buried on a beautiful sunny day, a Bank Holiday Monday and my father's forty-first birthday. The most painful day I will ever know.

If I was a child again?

If I could have one more day with her, this is what I would do.

I would play all of her favourite songs and I would never criticise. I would sing along to Barry Manilow and laugh with her as she told me of how she saw him on stage with his red piano like a dot in the distance of the huge arena, her first live concert in all her life.

I would take her to New York city, a place she longed to go to and we'd even fly down to Nashville and sing "Crazy" like we were both Patsy Cline.

I would go shopping with her, we would try on clothes, we would laugh at how things didn't fit no matter how much we wanted them to. We would go for coffee, we would stroll around like we didn't have a care in the world. Like her world had no end.

But I was just a child. I didn't know what God's plans were for me and my family. I didn't know that after that day I would never see her again.

Life goes on and time heals. So they say.

It does go on and it gets easier in that we learn to live with the pain, with the heartbreak, with the question of why life and why God would be so cruel to take away a mother from her six babies and from a husband who loved her so.

I am a mother too now and I am thirty-seven years old, just a few months older than she was when she died, and the thought of leaving my own three children at a time when I sometimes believe that my life is only beginning makes me realise just how much she has missed out on and how much we missed out on by not having her with us.

Does she know how we live now? Does she know she has six grandchildren as well as the six babies she gave birth to herself? Does she know some of us inherited her talent and are making a life writing in a way she always dreamed of? Does she know the men we each loved and lost and those we have loved again? Does she know how many people still talk of her with such disbelief that she is gone but with so many smiles around her memories?

Was she with us on the days of our exam results, when our children were born, did she see me when I launched my first novel, did she see her daughters on their wedding days, does she watch her only son when he sings in her honour at his gigs, does she watch over us on all the big milestones we come across . . . all the life-changing hurdles we have got over?

Does she see us sitting at her grave talking to her like she never left us in the first place?

Does she know how much every day we still miss her and how much our hearts ache to have her for just one more day?

If I was a child again I would cherish her more. I would understand that she was not only my mother but also a fantastic, funny, beautiful young person with her own needs and her own sacrifices and who was in the prime of her life, just as I feel I am now.

I would have done the washing-up that Friday evening. I would have nursed the baby more. I would have hugged her like there was no tomorrow because on that day there was no tomorrow.

For those of you who still have their mother, I look on you in so much envy. I watch my friends who visit their mothers, I watch as she becomes their best friend and their confidante and I still fight back the tears of what me, my sisters and my brother have lost out on. I watch my aunts look out for and enjoy their grandchildren in a way I only wish my own mother could have.

I imagine things all the time.

I imagine her every day.

I imagine how she would have looked now, the songs she would have loved now, how we would have spent time together and how she would have advised me and my brother and sisters on the choices we made in life and how she would have nurtured us and stood by us in any of the mistakes that we made.

I imagine how she would have made a career for herself when we were all a bit older and how she would have danced with my father and how they would have been lifelong companions and grown from those glamorous young parents who hoped and dreamed for easier times from the hardship of bringing up a young family.

I can hold on to my memories, but nothing holds you better than a mother's hug.

Give your mother a hug today . . . a really big one. And if she asks for something, big or small, do it for her if you can.

Emma Heatherington is from Donaghmore, County Tyrone, where she lives with her three children – Jordyn (17), Jade (12) and Adam (11). She works as a writer and freelance PR and has penned more than thirty short films, plays and musicals as well as seven novels for Poolbeg Press, two of which were written under the pseudonym Emma Louise Jordan. Emma has just completed her first feature film script which is in early development and her dream is to see it on the big screen with Liam Neeson in a lead role . . . Her favourite things, apart from writing and hanging out with her children, are all things Nashville (she is a self-confessed country music fanatic!), romantic comedy movies, sing-along nights with friends and family, red wine, musical theatre, new pyjamas, fresh clean bedclothes, long bubble baths and cosy nights in by the fire. Find Emma on Twitter @emmalou13 or on Facebook at emmaheatheringtonwriter.

It's a Small World

Gemma Jackson

I vividly remember sitting on our staircase landing. I was about three years old. We as a family had moved from the Dublin tenements a few months prior to this particular day. I still hadn't become accustomed to having our very own private staircase. I loved to sit on the landing and survey my own little world.

It was Friday. A very important day: it was comic day. I knew this because I heard my big sisters and brother talking. They were excited about having an inside toilet but I wasn't impressed by that. The staircase was a wonder to me.

I sat with my two feet on the stair underneath me. My back nestled securely into the stairway behind me. I could hear me da snoring in one of the bedrooms behind me. He was on night work so we had to be quiet. I wanted him to wake up.

I was intently watching the door at the bottom of the hall. I was so excited I was forgetting to breathe. Earlier me ma had put me baby sister in the pram and gone to the local shops.

I thought about going down the stairs and out into the big back garden. I wanted to but I was nervous. The garden of our new house was overgrown and full of stinging nettles. All the houses in the new scheme had the same problem. The men wanted to clear the space so they could plant gardens. A local farmer was lending his donkey and goats to anyone who wanted their gardens cleared. It was our turn to have the animals in our back garden. I'd sat up here and watched my brother drag the animals through the long hallway and out the back door. I'd felt safe up here watching the action.

I'd been sitting up here the other day when a man with a pony and trap came around the houses offering baby chicks for sale. I'd heard me ma say we'd be interested when the back garden was cleared. Everything was so new and different around our new house. I missed The Lane. I'd known everyone there and been allowed to go off with the other kids, but not here. Whenever I asked I just got told "not yet". I buried my head in my knees and, with my eyes fixed firmly on the front door, waited.

I heard our outside gate open. My sisters and brother exploded from the living room. I didn't rush down. They were bigger than me.

"Would you let me in the door for goodness' sake?" me ma snapped.

I stayed where I was. I could wait and from my vantage point I had a clear view of all the goings-on.

"Someone take these bags until I get the baby out of her pram. Seán, you take the bag with the comics. No peeking now. I want no trouble."

I stood with my face pressed between the stair rails and watched the bag with the precious comics being carried into the living room. The bag was put on the sofa. My brother and three older sisters stood in front of the sofa, patiently waiting.

"Right." My mother walked from the kitchen, pulling her scarf off her head. She'd removed her coat and was wearing her wraparound apron. My baby sister was on her hip, gnawing on something. "Let's see what we have here."

My mother put my sister down. She just stood there waiting. My mother sat on the sofa and pulled the comics from the bag.

"Who gets the *Jackie*?"

My eldest sister almost pulled tha...

"The *Dandy*?"

My brother grabbed that one. He escaped into the back with his comic. He wasn't afraid of the donkey and goats. They were easier to put up with than all those bloomin' sisters. I'd heard him say so.

"*Bunty*?" My mother held the comic aloft.

It too was pulled from her hand.

"*Judy*?"

That was snapped up.

"*Jack and Jill*?" My mother turned her head towards the staircase. She'd known I was there.

"Me," I tried to whisper and scream at the same time. I ran down the stairs and into the living room. My mother was passing *Playhour* to my youngest sister.

I grabbed my *Jack and Jill* with both hands and hurried back to my place on the stairs with my treasure. I couldn't read the comic yet but I could look at the pictures while I waited for one of my big sisters to be ready to read it to me.

I sat on the staircase, my precious comic open on my knees. The house was silent, everyone intent on reading. I turned the pages very carefully and examined the drawings and pictures in great detail. I became fascinated by the squares of drawings showing children with a small horse. It had its own house at the end of their garden.

I put my finger over each square and examined every little detail of this strange world. Why would a horse need its own house? Didn't horses live in fields like they did around where I lived now? We'd had a stable in The Lane but that was for working horses. This horse didn't look big enough to pull a cart. What would you do with a little horse like that?

I needed this story read to me. I looked down into the living room. No point asking my eldest sister. She'd give me a thick ear and tell me not to bother her. My next sister had a sweeter nature but she wasn't the fastest reader and my need was great. I'd have to beg the sister next in age to me. She was the best anyway but, Lord, she was cranky. I'd heard my mother say so. I didn't know that was what it was called to be in a bad mood all the time but I liked the word and it seemed to suit her.

I begged. I whined. I blubbered. I won. She read the story to me at a speed that would flatten you but I got the sense of the thing.

"It was too fast," I whispered to the next sister in age.

She put her own comic aside and took mine with a sigh. She read the story again slowly. She let me sit on the floor beside her and waited while I moved my fingers under the words. It was a magical tale.

"Will you read me this story, please?" I'd braved the donkey and goats. I'd do anything to hear this tale again.

My brother must have known it was important. After all, I'd ventured out to the back garden with the wild animals, hadn't I? He too read the story.

I took my comic back and turned to go inside and leave him in peace. I climbed back up the stairs. I opened my comic and visually examined every inch while keeping an eye on the living room. I had to wait until my sisters had finished reading their own comics. I continued to run my finger over the words written in white balloons coming out of the mouths of the children in the images.

Finally, after what seemed like days to me, my eldest sister started trying out new hairstyles she was copying from her comic. I gripped my comic tightly and slowly made my way down the stairs.

"Will you read this story to me, please?" I held up my comic.

"Did anyone ever tell you you're a nuisance?" she snapped.

"You do all the time," I answered honestly.

"Oh, give it here." She grabbed the comic from my hands and with a longsuffering sigh sat down on the floor in front of the fire.

I hadn't felt the cold until now but I was suddenly freezing. I shivered.

"Serves you right for sitting on those bloody stairs all day," my sister snapped. "You would think they were going to disappear on you or something."

I didn't answer her back or stick my tongue out – though I wanted to. She was the best at reading because she put on strange voices.

I sat enthralled while she read and acted out the story in my comic. I decided to sit quietly for a while before doing the rounds again. I couldn't get enough of this strange world in my colourful comic book.

When my sisters and brothers finally got angry at me I had to come up with another plan. I saw some of the older girls playing ball outside. I'd try and get the ones waiting for their turn to throw the balls against the wall to read my story. The plan worked. I passed my comic along the line and had my story read to me again and again.

My mother sent my eldest sister out to drag me in for something to eat. It still wasn't time for me da to wake up. I ate the stew when it was put in front of me and couldn't wait to try my luck with some of the other big kids.

"Do you want to wake your da up?" my mother shouted from the open front door.

"Yes!" I screamed.

I followed after my mother as she carried a cup of tea and a piece of bread she'd toasted on the open fire up the stairs. I almost stepped on her heels, I was following so close behind her.

"You better talk to this one." My mother opened the curtains to let in the light. I waited until me da moved in the bed. I knew I had to wait until he had almost half the big mug of tea drunk before I jumped on the bed. "She's been dragging around the place all day waiting for you to wake up." My mother left the room.

"What's that you've got?" me da said, pushing himself higher in the bed.

"It's me new comic, Da." I climbed up onto the bed with the comic in my hand. "Will you read it to me?"

"I'm only half awake, love," me da said.

"Do you want me to read it to you, Da?"

"Come here then, you maggot." Me da pulled me under his arm.

I opened my comic while he sipped his tea and ate the toast. I put my finger under the very first word and started to read aloud. I used my finger to follow every word. I was aware of me da listening intently and staring at the page. I felt so important.

"Rosie, come up quick!" Me da's roar almost deafened me. "Rosie, yeh gave birth to an honest to God genius . . . Rosie!"

"What's wrong?" my mother shouted up the stairs.

"Come up!" me da roared.

"In the name of God, what's up?" My mother ran up the stairs.

"Listen to our little genius." Me da nudged me. "Read the story again, love."

I did exactly that, feeling very important. For the first time in my life I was the sole focus of the attention of both parents.

"She's a fecking genius, Rosie!" me da yelled when I'd finished reading the story for the second time. "Not yet three years old and she's reading like a champion."

"She knows the ruddy story off by heart," my mother snapped. "She should do. She's had everyone and his brother pestered to read that ruddy story to her today."

"But she knows every word. She didn't make one mistake," my da continued to say. "We've got a genius on our hands." He patted the side of the bed. "Sit down a minute and listen to her read."

I was almost three years old and I'd discovered the power of the written word. I've never forgotten that feeling of power and the attention it gained me.

Gemma Jackson was born in inner-city Dublin, the fifth of seven children. She vividly remembers being taken to see the ships sail in and out of Dublin. Her mother would paint word pictures of exciting worlds filled with marvels beyond their little island. Educated by the nuns at Mount Sackville Convent in Castleknock, Gemma remembers a childhood of hunger, cold and desperation. Yet through it all, making life worth living, were wonderful people, stories, music and gales of laughter. The hardship of early childhood put steel in her spine. She first left home at seventeen, desperate to see what was out there, beyond the sea. She wanted to see the strange worlds her mother had spoken of, taste the weird food and learn everything she could of the wider world. She has travelled widely. Her debut novel *Through Streets Broad and Narrow* is a loving tribute to the Dublin she remembers.

Worrier

Susan Loughnane

I'm learning the breaststroke today. I feel like a frog swimming like this. Sometimes I get bored with it and float onto my back, close my eyes and imagine I am an otter floating in a lagoon. But then the instructor shouts at me and tells me to do what I'm supposed to be doing. I look up at the balcony where my dad is sitting, hoping he hasn't heard me being told off. I'd hate to make him disappointed. But he's chatting to another dad. He's laughing. He looks so happy. That's because he has just got a new job. But, shush, it's a secret. I hope he's not telling that man. I hope he remembers that we're not allowed to tell anyone until next week.

It was so hard today at school not telling everyone. We were doing "Our News" at the start of the school day where we tell the teacher our news and she writes it on the blackboard. *John has a new baby sister . . . Matthew got a new bike . . . Siobhán's big toenail fell off . . .* All of this was complete nonsense. I was sitting there about to explode with some really exciting news but I couldn't tell anyone. I wanted to shout it: *My dad got a new job! We'll be loaded! We're going on a holiday to France this summer!* But instead I sat on my hands and kept my mouth zipped shut like I promised.

Swim class is over. I wade to the edge of the swimming pool as fast as my skinny legs can move through the water and climb the steps at the corner. Still dripping wet, I race along the edge of the pool, past the instructor, who tells me to stop running. I want to tell him to stop frowning. I'm so excited about seeing my dad – to give him a big hug and go get choc-ice lollies like he promised. I run into the boys' changing room, as I always do when my dad collects me. But I can't see him; he must still be talking up on the balcony. Holy Moly, I hope that man he was talking to didn't push him over the balcony or something! Come to think of it, that man looked a bit like Jafar from *Aladdin*. He had a hooked nose and a skinny black moustache that slithered like a black worm down under his chin into a narrow beard. Maybe he's a bad guy. My poor Dad! He must not know that man is a baddie! Maybe I should go back out and look, and warn him . . . *Oh jeepers* . . . now I need to pee. Oh, I *really* need to go. I can feel it coming . . . a little bit trickles out and warms the underneath of my cold pink swimsuit. Oh no! I wrap my right leg around my left leg, squeezing them together. It would be so embarrassing to wee on the floor of the boys' changing rooms. I scuttle past the showers, hopping along somehow with my legs firmly squeezed around each other. Eventually I make it to the toilet and hobble straight into the nearest cubicle. I peel down my wet swimsuit and just about make it over the toilet bowl before I burst. *Phew!* That was a close call!

I reluctantly pull my cold, wet swimsuit back up and put the straps over my shivering shoulders. I'm so cold now my fingers are going purple and my toes are wiggling to stay warm. I keep thinking of my dad and Jafar. What if he has killed my dad and now he's coming for me and he has a hyena with him, and the hyena will do an evil cackle and then eat me? Oh, I can't bear to think about it any longer!

I push the door to get out and go find my dad, but it won't budge. It's jammed shut! I am trapped! *Forever!*

Hot tears stream down my face. I open my mouth wide, and release an almighty wail. This is it. Tragedy has befallen me. My life is over. I'll die in here, I just know it. But I'm too young and popular to die! Okay, I'm not really very popular, but I heard Jessica from *Sweet Valley High* say that on the telly and I thought it was such a cool thing to say. The big white wooden door looms threateningly in front of me. It seems so stern and unyielding. I'm seriously starting to panic. Suddenly I'm not cold any more, I'm hot and clammy and my little fists are banging on the enormous door. But it's futile; they're barely making a sound on the hard solid wood. But surely I'm making lots of noise with my shrieks and cries? Why is no one coming to help me? Does no one care? It's typical that no one in the boys' changing room is bothered. I hate boys. If I were in the girls' changing room they would be rushing to help me. I can't believe I'm going to die in here. My hands are starting to get sore. I'm now slapping the door wildly. My damp curly red hair is hanging in strings around my head, sticking to my neck and shoulders and falling into my eyes. I swipe my hair out of my face with my forearm while I'm still slapping the door with my hands.

But at last I have to stop. It's too painful. My hands are throbbing and stinging. I stop wailing too. I've accepted my fate. Still crying silent tears, I sit back down on the toilet, my whole body exhausted and totally devastated. I lift my feet onto the seat and wrap my arms around my knees, pulling them in to my chest, trembling with the cold. I've never been this sad in my whole life.

I lean my chin on my knees and look down at the chipped pink nail varnish on my toenails. Yesterday my Mam said that she would repaint them for our holiday in France and my feet would look like Princess feet. I wonder will my family go to France without me now? They won't be able to go without my dad, especially because they wouldn't be able to afford it without his new job. But maybe Dad is fine. Maybe it turns out Dad secretly has a magic flying carpet and he uses it to escape Jafar and safely land on the ground. Probably that would happen because Jafar could never outsmart my dad. My dad is the smartest man on Planet Earth. So my family will go to France without me after all. I'm sure they will be sad for a while . . . but they'll soon forget about me. My brothers will play football and swim in the pool without me . . . They might even be glad that I'm not there to annoy them. I'm always asking too many questions about everything, or singing too loudly, or repeating what they say in a high-pitched voice and then bursting into fits of giggles. Or maybe they'll miss having me there to run after the football for them when it goes far away. Maybe they'll find a new little sister over in France to replace me.

I'm now sobbing into my hands, thinking of life going on without me. Will they still buy *cinq croissants* from the baker and give my one to the new little sister? And after a while I'll be completely forgotten and I'll just be trapped in this big white wooden cubicle until I die a tragic and lonely death.

My whole body starts to shake and shiver. I suddenly start wailing again. I can't help it – it just comes up through my belly and out my mouth. An almighty roar.

"*Daddyyyy!* Save *meeeeee*! Don't leave me here! I want to come to France! I don't want to die! *Pleaseeee!*"

Suddenly a big strong familiar hand appears over the top of the door and with a heave it lurches open. My dad! He rushes in and embraces me in his big daddy arms and lifts me up into a bear hug. I can't believe it. It's the best moment of my whole entire life but I just can't stop crying. It's funny how that happens. Even though you're happy you cry uncontrollably. It happened to me another time when I found my black baby doll I thought I'd lost. But how I felt then doesn't even compare to this moment. Now I feel as though I'm going to explode with love and happiness. My dad carries me over to a bench and wraps me in a towel. I'm still sobbing and clinging onto him for dear life. My Superman Daddy has rescued me. I'm not going to die after all! When I can finally get my breath, I gasp and tell him, "I thought you were going to go to France without me!"

He smiles and combs my hair out of my eyes.

"Susie, I would never go to France without you."

This is a true story. I remember it vividly because I was so traumatised. I suppose it says a lot about how great my childhood was that the most traumatic thing that ever happened to me was the time I got stuck in a loo.

Reading back over the story I do realise how ridiculous it all seems that I got so carried away and actually believed I was going to die in the toilet cubicle of a public swimming pool. But at the time I really did believe that. It goes to show how active and extreme a child's imagination is, and that it must be both nurtured and protected.

Since then I have got stuck in a few more toilet cubicles over the years. But as I got older I learnt not to panic so much. I should probably take this opportunity to thank Pat the caretaker at Malahide Community School, who famously rescued me from the toilets of the junior block back in around 2004. That was a less traumatic, but considerably more embarrassing experience.

Even though I've got over my fear of hostage-taking loos, I still am, and always have been, a worrier. A catastrophist. I have an over-active imagination. As my mother says, I'm a "handwringer". But all of that makes me who I am. It contributes to my creativity and I wouldn't ever want it any other way.

Susan Loughnane first hit our screens as Debbie, the drug-addicted girlfriend of John Boy Power (Aidan Gillen) in RTÉ's hugely popular TV series *Love/Hate*. She won the 2013 IFTA for Best Supporting Actress for her performance in Series 3 of the show. She is also currently playing Chloe Chance in Channel 4's *Hollyoaks*. Susan is in the process of editing her first novel *Exhibit*, which she is very excited about. She is also co-writing a TV series set in London. If all this doesn't keep her busy enough she also has a job in London's Abercrombie & Fitch store but can't actually remember the last time she worked a shift. She resides between London, Liverpool and Dublin. She house-shares in Notting Hill, London, with two humans and a community of mice. She also has ownership of a drawer in a house in Ennis, County Clare, where she hopes to live some day. Susan is really thrilled to be involved in this project for Barnardos and hopes you enjoy her story.

'Twas the Night Before Christmas

Marisa Mackle

It was the night before Christmas. And not a creature was stirring. Well, nobody besides me of course. You see, I was determined to see Santa. I didn't care how long I had to stay awake. I just *had* to see him this year. The previous year my younger sister had seen him. So she told me anyway. Not only had she seen him, but she had engaged in a lengthy chat with him. She related all this to me with her big blue eyes full of genuine sincerity. Who was I to doubt my sweet little six-year-old sibling?

But deep down I couldn't help feeling a teeny-weeny bit jealous. I mean, yes, I was pleased for her. I was definitely pleased. However, I myself had been a very good girl all year also, and yet Santa had just left my present, a toy safari, at the end of the bed without even bothering to say hello. The least he could have done was tap me on the shoulder and give me a quick "How's it going?" Yes, I understood he was busy. Run off his feet in fact, along with all the elves and Rudolf. And of course I knew that he had to deliver thousands and thousands of presents to kids all around the world in just one single night. But surely he could have had just a two-minute chat with me? Or even a thirty-second chat? Why had he chosen my sister over me? What did she have that I didn't have?

Of course these days, if I met a big celebrity like Santa, I know I'd be whipping out my mobile phone to take a photo with him. Just to prove to everyone that I had actually met him. I'm sure a photo of the two of us could even be my profile photo on Facebook! But back then, when my prize possession was a second-hand cassette player, and there was just one heavy black phone in the hall under the stairs, and everybody smoked in the cinema and on airplanes, and it was the seventies, all I wanted was a face-to-face chat with the big man himself.

Okay, so I was fairly familiar with the essence of Mister Claus. I mean, I had met Santa myself a couple of times in the now long-gone Switzers department store after queuing for several hours to meet him. I had even been presented with a badge to wear that read, *"I met Santa at Switzers"*. But I knew that he wasn't the real Santa. The real Santa lived in the North Pole with his wife and Rudolph and all his little helpers. He didn't need to be wasting time in shopping centres handing out cheap plastic toys and going, *"Ho, ho, ho!"* That's why he had representatives in shops. They were only men who looked like him. They were large and jolly with red suits and black boots and long white beards. And sometimes they invited you to sit on their knee. But they weren't *him*.

I was envious of my sister for having met Santa personally. She seemed to have all the luck when meeting kiddie "celebs". Not only had she met and spoken to the great man himself, but she had also met the Tooth Fairy several times and the Easter Bunny on occasion. It just wasn't fair. I had met nobody except Bosco, the puppet from RTÉ with the annoying voice.

Anyway, this one year, I had made up my mind. I was going to meet Santa in person no matter what it took. Of course, I loved everything about Christmas. I loved the fact that we made Christmas lanterns at school, and that Mum made the cake weeks and weeks in advance, and that she also started buying the presents as early as October because, as she always said,

Christmas came upon you too fast. I looked forward to hanging up my advent calendar above my bed and opening a window every day until it was Christmas Eve. I enjoyed learning the Christmas hymns in the classroom and picking out what I was going to wear on Christmas morning to Mass with my family. But of course meeting Santa would top all this. It was the ultimate goal.

I made out many lists to Santa. I would write out a list of things I wanted and then scrunch the piece of paper in a ball and throw it in the bin. Then I would write another list and another one. I kept changing my mind about what I wanted.

I felt bad about messing Santa around with my endless lists being left up the chimney but, in all honesty, I didn't want to ask him for too much. I knew that he had to get presents for kids all around the world, and although he had a whole year to source everything, it must have been quite a challenge. Of course, he had all his helpers but, still, he was old and he wasn't in the best of shape with that big belly on him. I for one could never figure out how he managed to squeeze down our narrow chimney. And didn't all the soot dirty his snowy white beard?

A toy that was very popular at the time was an Etch-A-Sketch, on which you could do your own drawings and then erase them. I had seen ads for them on TV and had decided I wanted one for myself. When Mum asked me whether I had yet decided what I wanted from Santa, I told her I'd made up my mind. I wanted an Etch-A-Sketch.

"What's that?"

"It doesn't matter. Santa will know exactly what it is. He knows everything about toys."

Poor Mum. If I was a child again I would tell my mum exactly what I had asked Santa to bring me. I wouldn't keep it such a big secret!

Mum also asked my sister what she wanted from Santa.

"I want it to be a surprise," she stated firmly. "I only want Santa to know, so it will be a surprise for everyone on the day. Even you, Mummy."

The night before Christmas was terribly exciting. We stood outside on the porch and looked up at all the stars on that cold frosty night. A few of the stars were twinkling furiously in the sky.

"I wonder which one is Santa's sleigh?" I said.

I thought I saw it moving across the sky. Then again it might have been a plane. The sky is always full of planes bringing people home for Christmas. I hoped Santa would remember to bring my Etch-A-Sketch. I didn't want him to mix it up with another kid's present and leave it in the wrong home. It must have been difficult to remember which presents belonged in which house. How did he even know where he was supposed to leave everything?

In our house he always left the presents at the end of the beds. But in the house next door he left the presents under the tree. In our house he always had a whiskey and large slice of Christmas cake. Next door he never failed to enjoy some milk and biscuits. No wonder he was a bit fat. Everywhere he went Santa seemed to eat and drink. In our house he always came down the chimney but a friend of mine lived in an apartment that didn't have a chimney, so in her home he always took the lift up to her floor and let himself in the door. It really was amazing how he remembered what was what and who was who. No wonder he didn't have time for frivolous chats with people! In fact, apart from my little sister, I hadn't met anyone else who had spoken to Santa in real life.

The night before Christmas I was wide awake. My mum and dad had kissed me goodnight and had told me they'd see me in the morning. As they turned out the light I smiled to myself. Sleep? As if! I didn't care how long it would take, there was no way on earth I was dozing off and missing my big chance to chat with Santa.

The minutes passed. So did the hours. It was so dark and quiet, but my eyes were open, and my ears were cocked. I was looking out for shadows. Or the sound of Rudolph's bell tinkling. But there was still no sign. I told myself to be patient. Santa would be arriving no matter what. He didn't come on any night other than Christmas Eve. Soon enough I'd hear his footsteps on the carpet of my bedroom floor.

Suddenly the door opened. Just a tiny bit, but enough to allow the light from the hallway to flood my room. My heart almost stopped. Oh God, was it him? Was it really him at last? The excitement was overwhelming.

"Santa? Is that you?" My voice quivered.

But it wasn't Santa. It was Dad. He sounded tired.

"Go to sleep now, Marisa. He's not here yet."

"Is he on his way?"

"Yes."

An hour later I thought I heard his footsteps on my bedroom floor.

"Santa?"

"No, love."

It was Mum. I was beyond disappointed. Why did my parents keep coming into my room? They were probably putting Santa off! Maybe Santa didn't want to feel forced to enjoy a whiskey with Dad down in the kitchen? Or get into a boring conversation with Mum? I didn't want to hurt their feelings but I just wished they would go off to bed and leave me in peace.

I waited and I waited. And every now and then I would sneak to the window, pull back the curtain and gaze at the sky. Where was he? I was so tired. I didn't know how much longer I could keep awake without succumbing to my yawns.

Sometime later sleep took over. I drifted off. But I must have been just dozing lightly because suddenly I heard my bedroom door shut and I bolted upright in the bed. My feet hit something heavy. There was a present. Oh God, he was here! I jumped up and ran to the bedroom door, flinging it open. I raced down the stairs and burst into the kitchen.

Mum and Dad were standing at the sliding doors, waving out at the night.

"Bye, Santa!" they shouted in unison.

I was gobsmacked. I just stared at my parents in disbelief. Mum was wearing a nightie and Dad had his pyjamas and a dressing gown on. They both looked exhausted.

"He was here?" I was incredulous.

"Yes, he's just gone," Mum said. "He said he had to fly."

"You mean you spoke to him?"

They both nodded. I rushed to look out the doors but there wasn't a sign of Santa's sleigh anywhere in the starry night.

Then I glanced down at the Christmas cake. It was untouched. Santa hadn't taken his usual slice? But he *always* had cake in our house!

"He wasn't all that hungry," Dad explained gently. "Too many people offered him a slice of cake this year. Now let's all go to bed."

"Do you want to see my presents?"

"We can see them later," Mum insisted. "We all need to get some sleep now."

Dad looked at his watch – it was now five o'clock in the morning – and nodded in agreement. He'd had enough of the drama.

Marisa Mackle is the author of seventeen books including *Along Came a Stork* and *The Secret Nanny Club*. She has published two children's books illustrated by former Miss World, Rosanna Davison, called *Girl in the Yellow Dress* and *Lucy Goes to Hollywood*. She is also a columnist for the *Evening Herald* and *Enterprise* magazine. She has a son, Gary, and two and a half cats (one cat divides her time between Marisa and a neighbour). She has a degree in English literature from UCD and now guest-lectures herself at universities. She is currently published in fourteen different languages, including Japanese and Russian, and is a number one bestseller in Ireland and Germany. Her favourite pastimes are shopping, travel, water sports, and of course, reading! She loves everything to do with Christmas and always puts up her (artificial!) tree the day after Halloween. For more information see www.marisamackle.ie.

If Only . . .

Mary Malone

What would I do if I were a child again, if *only* for one day?

Everything? Anything? Something I was afraid to try back then? Something wild or crazy that was strictly forbidden? Something old-fashioned like playing hide-and-seek, transforming a rusty wheelbarrow into a golden chariot or trying to decipher messages from the rustling of leaves in the wind?

My brain is a muddle, my heart is pounding with excitement and I can't stand still. The promise of one day without responsibility or conscience, one day to hop, skip and jump in puddles, one whole day to have a licence to climb trees and hang upside-down seems too good to be true. The real treat about a return to childhood of course is the immense thrill of *not* being an adult, *not* acting appropriately and *not* giving a second thought to what other people think.

Unleashing long-forgotten memories and dreams, I slip back into the world of make-believe that accounted for a significant amount of my early childhood. Jumping on a spaceship travelling to an undiscovered planet is top of my list, clad of course in the appropriate "tin-foil" outfit that every self-respecting space-visitor wears! The prospect of floating around the universe and snatching a glimpse of the local "planet people" is exciting in itself but the ultimate wish for this temporary return to childhood is to fulfil a lifetime desire to meet real-life aliens!

I have so many questions for those little green people. What's life like up there beyond the clouds? Can they see us earthlings? Do they control us from a distance? Can they become invisible and make things happen on Earth just for laughs? Do they cause us to stumble over our own feet or fall out of bed for no reason? I would love to find out if they're responsible for making wishes come true, or is it really enough to close your eyes and visualise? And more than anything I want to convince an alien to come home and live with me – if only for that one day (blame watching numerous repeats of *E.T. the Extra-Terrestrial* on that one!). No doubt, now that I think of it, times have changed for aliens too and instead of devising a contraption to "phone home" my alien would be texting or social networking with fellow aliens.

Or perhaps if there's no spaceship available, I could spend my day riding a huge white horse, clinging on to her mane for dear life as she gallops at lightning speed over ditches and across streams and raising my arms high in the air when we come to an elaborate and dramatic stop at the end of a vivid rainbow. Now that would be amazing, particularly as the only time I ever tried to ride a horse I was around five years old and the gigantic animal sensed my fear and took off through trees, my screams of terror doing nothing to help the situation apart from encouraging him to run even faster so that by the time I eventually fell off, I was scraped, stung and grazed all over from tree branches, nettles and briars. As for my pride, I'm not sure that has ever truly recovered, but the modern-day concern for health, safety and clinical cleanliness simply didn't exist then – let's just say once you could pick yourself up off the ground and your limbs were still attached, most falls went unnoticed.

But galloping horses, spaceships and aliens are all figments of my very vivid imagination and while the idea of using that one special day to defy reality and escape into a world of fantasy is appealing, I'm concerned I may be wasting an extraordinary opportunity to rewrite history. What if there's a way to rejuvenate some of my unbridled childhood spirit (from the era before the galloping horse story) and transport it to 2013 to the adult I am today?

How strong is the link between childhood and adulthood? Is there any possibility that the antics and actions in our earliest years play a significant role in the adults we become? At what point in our lives do we lose the fearlessness we're born with? Is there a specific defining moment for all of us? Or are life experiences responsible for the gradual erosion of our dreams? Perhaps it's the people and obstacles we come in contact with that alter our perspective and diminish our belief that anything is possible and within reach if we want it badly enough. Would a trip further down memory lane help me recognise the twists and turns along the path of my life that obliterated options?

To try and describe this notion further, a cone-shaped party hat comes to mind. As a child I spent more time looking through them than wearing them on my head (I never could bear the confining feel of elastic around my throat). Viewing through the narrow end with a child's perception on life shows the world as a magical place to be explored. As adults (sadly), we frequently look through the cone in the opposite way, tunnelling our vision as we focus on the road ahead. But an opportunity to look at the world through a child's eyes again would not only be spectacular, it would be transforming.

"What will you do when you grow up?" is one of the most common questions a young child is asked. And with the precious commodity of innocence still intact, the answers are mostly entertaining and far-reaching, have nothing to do with the economy or where business or industry is heading but everything to do with what fires the excitement within the child at that point in time when everything seems possible and curiosity and simplicity are the order of the day.

Looking back on more of those fun-filled childhood days, my greatest unfiltered memories (unsurprisingly as it has turned out) are the endless hours I spent lost in books and escaping to imaginary worlds with my favourite author, Enid Blyton (undoubtedly the real reason I'm an author today). With books in short supply at times, I was content to read the same stories over and over until the world of midnight feasts, tuck boxes, mysterious noises in the night and of course the happy-ever-after endings merged with reality. Re-reading seemed to extend the enjoyment I got from these tales and as a result, The Naughtiest Girl, Famous Five, Secret Seven, Mallory Towers, ghosts and goblins and an expanse of magic from the pages of these books provided the basis for hours of imaginary play with cousins (girl cousins that is – the boys were too busy playing Cowboys and Indians, three-goals-in, penalty shootouts and tug of war with my brother).

Needless to say, our parents were quick to let out a fairly stern shout (little concern in my family about hurting your feelings) when they discovered the bed linen missing off the beds and being used as a mattress in the tree house or a cover for the person on lookout as they waited for whatever baddie we were expecting to attack. Collectively, we (boys and girls on these occasions) became sprint runners when a *sliotar* went through a window or, even worse, when somebody's hand went through a pane of glass because they had been mysteriously 'shoved' as somebody passed them out in an all-important game of chasing, minutes before the cousins had to leave.

Freedom, hours of uninterrupted play and lots of laughter and squabbling sums up these memories. Keenly aware, however, that I'm assessing them now through rose-tinted glasses, I force myself to play good cop/bad cop and unlock a few horrible moments too – the cruel jokes from schoolfriends or the disappointments when I lost a race or came last in a competition even though I'd tried my hardest; the places I wasn't allowed go and the fury when I thought my parents were stricter than everybody else's and were being totally unrealistic. On this last example, I can confirm that I know better now and they certainly knew better then!

Nothing unique in my childhood memories, I've no doubt, yet as an adult and a parent looking back I recognise that despite the simplistic nature of those days and the absence of any great materialism, I took for granted the wealth and importance of what mattered most – an inordinate sense of freedom and the opportunity to seize the magic of being a child without a care or concern in the world.

Initially writing two thousand words on this topic seemed a simple task, an idea I could almost write in my sleep – until I sat down to put words on a page. In truth, I found it one of the most complicated pieces of writing I have ever put together. What I've realised on my trip down memory lane is that despite arguing otherwise at times, childhood sets the foundations for our future, our families provide the cornerstones and values we carry with us through life and, for me at least, the praise and criticism I received in my earliest years still lurk in the recess of my mind waiting to nudge against my confidence or fears at the most unexpected of times.

But given a chance now (in 2013) to be a child for one more day, I'm wondering how best to conquer that magical opportunity with the additional trappings available to children in today's technological world. In fact, I'm dubious if this modern era could provide equivalent magic – wouldn't gadgets and social media be too much of a distraction? Or perhaps my adult cynicism is once more narrowing my vision and blocking my view of a new and improved world where party hats no longer have silly elastic strings and galloping horses come with a *stop* button!

All things considered, certain facts remain the same: children run and jump and skip, play with their friends and cousins and savour the long school holidays. Being a child in today's world is filled with the newest and latest in computer games, communication, advertising and the inability to keep up . . . but it isn't really about what we have or have not, it's about our perception of life and which end of the cone we hold to our eye.

For those children relying on the help of Barnardos' excellent facilities, resources and support, I hope that one day they too get to look back and remember their childhood with warmth and positive emotion.

Mary Malone lives in Templemartin, Bandon, County Cork with her husband, Pat, and sons, David and Mark. As well as being a novelist and freelance journalist, she works full time in the Central Statistics Office. Mary's fifth novel, *Where There's A Will*, was published by Poolbeg in April 2013. Currently she is also very busy ghost-writing a non-fiction book due into the shops by Christmas 2013. For more information, please email: mary@marymalone.ie or visit her website, www.marymalone.ie

Holidays

Miranda Manning

I know we all remember childhood summer holidays as permanent sunshine, though there must have been rain. I remember one holiday when there was rain for a solid week, but that was the exception. One week out of a whole Irish summer wasn't bad.

For several years my family rented a house about nine miles from where we lived. This was not a holiday home in the current sense of the term. It was one of four houses which were literally just about thirty yards from the edge of a cliff. The others were sometimes occupied by other families who became friends over the years and cards would arrive at Christmas or birthdays from Tipperary or Cork City from our holiday friends even though we never met them during the year. One year we got the largest house and the other three were occupied by a pack of Boy Scouts. I'm sure my mother was disappointed that year because her holiday friends weren't there.

The houses weren't very well equipped so we had to bring some of our own furniture. We didn't have a car at the time so my parents had to hire an open-backed small truck to take us there. Some of my older sisters and my brother would cycle, as far as I recall. Our parents travelled in the cab with the driver and I and at least one sister or cousin or friend travelled in the back with the mattresses, beds, a few chairs, assorted pots and pans and our jet-black cat. Keeping the cat from jumping out of the open-topped trailer was a job in itself and I remember being rigid with fright in case he succeeded.

The first day would be spent assembling beds, unpacking food and deciding who would sleep where. Once we were unpacked it was total freedom. There were only a few houses near the beach and the nearest village was about a mile away along the cliff. Going by road was much longer. There was another village about two miles away by road. I have no recollection of how we got groceries delivered but my parents must have organised it some way (though there was no phone) because we were all fed and watered with the same regularity as we had been at home. In any case my mother, who was a great cook, was able to feed the multitudes with the very limited mod cons that were there. In retrospect I often wonder what she got out of the holiday. It seems to me that her work was harder and she wasn't the outdoor type. I only remember her in a swimsuit (or "swimming togs" as we called them then) once and she sat on the rocks with her feet in a rock pool. It was my father who was into swimming and rock-climbing. A strong swimmer himself, he taught us all to swim – some more successfully than others.

It was my first experience of dining *al fresco*. We had breakfast outdoors every day that was fine enough. Not exactly patio furniture. There was a large field in front of the houses, between them and the cliff, and we carried out the kitchen table and had our Corn Flakes out there. It was in the days before pasteurised milk and the only milk available was goat's milk which we got from a woman called Mrs Patsy two fields away. She kept two or three goats and always had plenty of spare milk. I never liked goat's milk and it hadn't yet been discovered as a health food. The weird taste took a bit from the pleasure of eating Corn Flakes in the open air. But that's just a small quibble.

I think it was the only thing I didn't like about those holidays. I never figured out whether Patsy was a surname or a Christian name but I think she was married to a guy whose Christian name was Patsy. She had no children herself and always gave us a great welcome, sometimes providing a scone to eat on our way back home.

The days seemed endless – particularly during the hot summers. We swam, climbed, collected shells, built sandcastles and explored to our hearts' content. When the tide was out we played our own versions of cricket, hurling and tennis. We carefully marked out the pitch or tennis court on the wet sand even though we didn't have any measuring tape so we couldn't have got the dimensions right. I didn't really like cricket or hurling and was usually the last to be picked on a team. I had great difficulty hitting such a small ball with a hurley or a cricket bat. I was a bit more successful with the tennis racquet – there was a lot of debate about whether my shots actually got over the imaginary net but at least I hit the ball! Come to think of it, looking back now our days were quite repetitive but I don't ever remember being bored. We just enjoyed it. There seemed to be no fear of drowning or falling from the cliffs. The only rules we had to adhere to was not to swim until at least an hour after having a meal, not to swim near the rocks, and always to swim parallel to the shore. Our parents seemed to think that there were few dangers and maybe they were right. I don't remember anybody ever being drowned on that beach, which subsequently became very popular. Most weekdays the beach was deserted except for ourselves and our holiday friends. But on Wednesday afternoons and Saturdays and Sundays there might be about twenty carloads of people from nearby towns when businesses were closed and people had time off from work. In some ways we considered this akin to an invasion of our territory, given that we almost regarded that particular strand as our private property. The bad bit about that attitude was that, on the days when the townspeople came, our father insisted that we pick up any rubbish they left behind and dispose of it correctly. He was the first person I ever met who had a sense of keeping the environment as nature intended and was decades before his time in that regard. I don't ever remember using sunscreen, but there was a white cream made by Nivea which some people on the beach used to cool down, after the damage was done. To this day the smell of a Nivea product brings me back to those days on the strand. We did occasionally wear sunhats but my memory is that we lived in our swimsuits and if it got cooler we donned shorts and tee-shirts. We were all fairly sallow-skinned so we never got sunburned, but I do remember a woman from the town getting badly sunburned on one hot Wednesday and there was no remedy immediately available.

We had the most brilliant picnics. We had an enormous white enamel bread bin with a red lid and on really fine days we would fill that up with sandwiches and bring bottles of lemonade and a few flasks for the adults and we would spend the whole day on the beach without returning to the house for anything. On a good day there might also be chocolate or apple tart but that was rare enough. My older sisters sometimes brought a book and there would be uproar if they lost a library book. This sometimes happened if someone accidentally or even deliberately (as I recall doing on at least one occasion) buried a book in the sand. The librarian was a really nice man but he didn't take kindly to lost books and was religious in his fervour about applying fines, so someone cycled into town every fortnight to change the books.

In the evenings after the day on the beach we usually just went back home and played cards or read and, being the youngest, I was always the first to be sent to bed. When the weather was particularly fine we were allowed to stay up later than usual when the mackerel and sprats came in and we watched people fishing from the beach. Sometimes our father caught some fish and we ate them for lunch the following day. I remember one year racing down to the beach to see the mackerel because they had come in late. I was at the rear of the group being the smallest and for some reason the cat followed us.

While we were watching the men fishing the cat dipped his front paw delicately into the rock pools and caught the occasional slow-swimming shrimp. This didn't appear to be a violent act, which of course it was, but a slow graceful dance that was carried out with amazing precision. I found it interesting that the cat instinctively knew what to do. Where had he ever seen a shrimp before and how did he know it was a fish? Some of our friends collected periwinkles and brought them home to be cooked. My mother never encouraged us to do this. I think she may not have relished the thought of putting them into boiling water alive. Similarly she never cooked or ate lobster in her life as far as I know.

One summer that I remember we did get a very wet week. We had a cousin visiting from Leeds who was a little older than us and who we thought was the height of sophistication. He cycled the nine hilly miles to the nearest town in the pouring rain and bought us all colouring books and pens and pencils and paints. He was a talented artist and before the week was over he had taught the older ones how to draw cartoons and the younger ones how to colour between the lines. My mother would have applied to have him canonised if she knew how.

About once a week, at around eight o'clock at night, when the weather permitted, somebody (I don't know who) brought a wooden platform to the beach and put it on a flat grassy patch away from the sea and sand. Three or four musicians would come and people would arrive in dribs and drabs by bike and car and the occasional horse and cart and the dancing would begin. It was mainly céilí and old-time waltzing but it was great fun, especially for me as it was the only night I was allowed to stay up as late as my sisters.

I have no clear memory of how long these holidays lasted, whether it was two weeks, four weeks or more. Several years when the holiday was over but the weather remained good we stayed on for up to two weeks into September. Our father would cycle several miles to the bus stop each day and get the bus to work while we remained on in the beach house. When we arrived back in school two weeks after everybody else the teachers were none too pleased but our parents believed that childhood should be about fun, and in any case there was a lot of education to be had by communing with nature. I'm not sure they ever convinced our teachers but in the end they just accepted it.

The nature of holidays has changed in many ways since the days when my family spent the summers on holidays nine miles from where we lived.

Advice to children: If you are enjoying something, live in the moment and don't worry about the future. If you are unhappy or sad for more than a few days tell a trusted adult. They will almost certainly be able to help.

Miranda Manning took up writing many years ago when she was a stay-at-home mum. For the first year or two she had little success but when the first magazine arrived in her letterbox with her story in it, she was over the moon. Since then she has had a number of stories and articles published in magazines and newspapers both in Ireland and the UK. She also has had flash fiction published in a charity book called *Celebrating What Really Matters* in aid of the Irish Hospice Foundation (Christmas 2011) and she contributed a short story to the charity collection *All I Want for Christmas* in aid of Barnardos (Christmas 2012). She lives in Galway and has three adult children all of whom have flown the coop. Her debut novel *Who is Alice?* was published by Poolbeg in May 2013.

My Big Regret

Eugene McEldowney

When I look back, I realise that I would change very little about my childhood. I grew up in a time of austerity far worse than people are experiencing now. I had few of the material comforts that most children today take for granted. There were no computer games, no mobile phones, no Facebook, no videos, no television. Many of our neighbours experienced real hardship, even hunger. Yet my memories of that time are largely happy ones. I was blessed to be part of a loving family and I felt secure.

Belfast in the late 1940s, shortly after the end of the Second World War, was a place of severe shortages. Parts of the city were wastelands after they were bombed by the Luftwaffe in two air raids that killed over a thousand people and demolished whole streets of houses. Food, clothes, even basic commodities like bread were rationed. The ration book became a very important item in every household. Everybody was issued with one and to purchase even a small bar of chocolate you had to give the shopkeeper a stamp along with your cash.

But I never remember going hungry. My father was an electric welder which was a trade in steady demand after the war so he was rarely out of work. And my mother was a thrifty housewife who was well able to produce nourishing meals from very little. She was also an expert in recycling, way before it became fashionable. Worn clothes were cut up and turned into short trousers and little jackets for me and my two brothers on her sewing machine.

We never felt out of place wearing these home-made clothes. Everyone else was wearing them so what was the difference? It wasn't as if people had the money to buy new ones even if they were available. It was 1954 before rationing was lifted and people were able to get their hands on brand-new clothes.

The same thing applied to consumer goods. There were two hundred houses on our street and only two cars. One was an old-fashioned black London taxi and the other was a Morris Minor, which belonged to a salesman who presumably got it as a condition of his job. There were no televisions. I remember the first one to arrive on our street and the crowds of children gathering, not to see the television itself but to gaze in awe at the aerial on the roof.

The area where we lived was Ardoyne in the north of the city. It was a large Catholic neighbourhood dominated by two symbols that remain forever etched in my mind. One was the twin spires of Holy Cross church looking down on the long rows of little terraced houses. The other was the linen mills which provided a lot of the employment in the area, mainly for women.

The linen mills were going strong when I was a little boy. I can still remember the loud wail of the hooters sounding out over the district to announce the start of a new working day and the lines of mill-girls, linking arms and singing as they went to work. But already, the mills were doomed by technology and the invention of new synthetic fibres. By the time I had grown to become an adult, they had all closed their large forbidding-looking gates and the hooters had fallen silent.

You might think with the deprivations we faced we would have been unhappy. Far from it. We had everything we needed in our cosy little world. We had toys, not the flashy, expensive toys of today but little motor-cars that you wound up and scooters that you pedalled with your foot and skates and marbles and footballs, even a bicycle. We had plenty of friends. People had big families so there were always loads of children to play with. I was never short of company.

And we had plenty of things to entertain us. In the 1950s, Ardoyne was almost open countryside. There were fields to explore and every Sunday my father would take us for walks to Carr's Glen or by tram to Cave Hill from where we could look down on the entire city. There were two public parks nearby with swings and slides and sandpits to play in. There were several cinemas within walking distance that held Saturday matinees where we could watch Gene Autry ride his horse into the sunset and laugh at the hilarious antics of the Three Stooges and Abbot and Costello.

And we had a public library with a children's section where I could lose myself for hours, engrossed in the adventures of Jim Hawkins in *Treasure Island* or Huckleberry Finn sailing his raft down the Mississippi river. It is to that library on the Oldpark Road that I owe my love of reading which I have carried with me throughout my life and which has never left me.

There were lots of other diversions to keep our young minds occupied. There was Smithfield market where my father would often take us on a Saturday afternoon. It was like Aladdin's cave: stalls of second-hand books, used clothes, antiques and knickknacks of all sorts including German helmets from the war, Samurai swords, even discarded sashes that the Orangemen wore on their annual excursions every July 12th to celebrate the Battle of the Boyne.

There was the Ulster Museum at the Botanic Gardens with its glass cases of antiquities, home to the fabled Mummy Woman whose display we always approached with fascination mingled with fear and trepidation. I have since learned that her real name was Takabuti and she lived in the Egyptian city of Thebes almost 3000 years ago. She arrived in Belfast in 1835, having been exhumed from her Egyptian resting place by a local Egyptologist called Thomas Greg.

During the summer holidays there were trips to seaside resorts like Bangor and Portrush where we got to travel by steam train, which was an adventure in itself. Like most little boys, I never remember wind or rain but only long sunny days and sunburn and the treat of fish and chips and Coca Cola in Morelli's cafe when the day was over.

Ardoyne was a safe place to grow up in the 1950s. Crime was relatively minor and murder practically unheard of. I can only remember one murder case and it kept the city enthralled for months. As I have said, there were few cars so traffic accidents were rare. Our only brush with the law occurred when we played football on the street and the sight of a policeman would cause us all to run and hide in case he took our names and wrote them down in his notebook.

Like many things in Belfast, education was segregated along religious grounds. The Catholic children went to the local school and the Protestants went to their schools across the Crumlin Road. Sad to relate but in a city with a Protestant majority in the 1950s, I never had a single Protestant friend till I went to Queen's University many years later. And not only were we divided along religious grounds but we were also segregated according to gender. The boys had one school and the girls had theirs.

I have no bad memories of school. The teachers were largely dedicated and enthusiastic. Corporal punishment was rare and only used in cases of serious misconduct. I was a good student and my interests in reading and composition were encouraged. It was at school that a music teacher called Dermot Maginness selected me for the church choir and I will always owe a debt to the hours he spent training us to sing.

But it is in my schooldays that I find the one big thing I would change if I was a child again. We were all working-class boys, many of us tough and streetwise and occasionally cruel. But there was one boy who didn't fit into this category. He was a small, shy, nervous boy with a shock of dirty brown hair. His name was Ambrose Skelly.

Ambrose seemed to be devoid of most of the skills required to survive in the environment he found himself in. He was useless at football and most boyish games. He couldn't fight. He wasn't clever. He couldn't tell jokes to make us laugh. There was nothing exciting or interesting about him. And, unlike most of us, he had no brothers at the school to protect him. Poor Ambrose was the perfect victim.

His name alone would have singled him out. I know now that St Ambrose was a highly regarded doctor of the early Christian church. But none of us had ever heard of him before and the name lent itself to jibes. Ambrose – Bendy-nose. His surname was even worse. Skelly – Rubber-belly or Skelly-eyes (meaning squinty or cross-eyed).

But what really damned Ambrose was his stammer. I'm sure he must have had nightmares when called upon by the teacher to read out loud. It might take a full minute before he could even speak and then it was a painful stumbling and struggling before he succeeded in getting a sentence out. Meanwhile, the tittering and sniggering would spread through the class like wildfire till at last poor Ambrose, his face red from embarrassment, would sit down again.

I don't know why the teacher persisted in asking him to read. Maybe it was a belief that it would cure his stammer. Perhaps it was to show that he was no different to the rest of us, which he clearly was. But it must have been hell for Ambrose.

There is a kind of animal wildness that can sometimes grip young boys when they are in groups and lead them to do things they wouldn't normally do on their own. Ambrose felt the full brunt of it. At break times, gangs would often gather round him in the schoolyard and taunt him. They would make fun of his stammer. They would call him names. Occasionally they would shove and push him. He was like a wounded hare surrounded by a pack of dogs.

I knew this was wrong and I didn't join in. But I did nothing to stop it either. It might have been self-preservation, a fear that told me if I sided with Ambrose I could be next for the same treatment. I don't know why he didn't report it to the teachers. Perhaps he felt it would only make matters worse because snitches were despised in the school. I don't know if the teachers were even aware of it. Maybe Ambrose believed if he did nothing, it would eventually stop.

But I have always regretted that I wasn't brave enough to go to him and put my arm around his shoulder and tell him I was his friend and he was not alone. I don't know why I didn't speak out against the bullies. I feel ashamed now that I stood by and did nothing.

I lost track of Ambrose Skelly when I left at age eleven to go to grammar school. Years later, I asked about him and was told that he had emigrated to London. I never saw him again. But I have never forgotten him or his pale haunted face as he cowered from the taunts of the schoolyard bullies. I hope he found peace in his later life. I hope the treatment he endured never happens to another child.

Eugene McEldowney is a former journalist with the *Irish Times* where he held the position of night editor. He is the author of fifteen published novels. He is a well-known singer on the traditional music circuit.

Custard Beasties and Other Despicable Things

Siobhán McKenna

My favourite pastime was mud. Playing with it, wetting it, moulding, eating it. If there was a mud pile around I probably wasn't far away. My favourite playmates were boys. For a time the two collided; I got to play with mud and boys. Life was fun and dirty in the cleanest possible sense.

I blame it on my father. If he'd wanted a son, I'd never have guessed. Instead, I remember the pride in his voice, as he spoke with his Cork lilt. "I'm the only male in the household. Except for the cat, Claudius. They" [my mother, my sisters and me] "gave him the snip and changed his name to Cleo. So you see, it's safer to keep quiet around here," he'd declare and cross his legs for emphasis.

I would have liked to be a boy. Thankfully, undeterred by tradition, Dad bought me train sets, Scalextric racing cars, and Buckaroo. I loved them.

"Your mother says Sindy is derogatory to women and will give you the wrong aspirations for life," he'd say, handing me a fishing rod.

I didn't have a clue what he was on about and I didn't care. I loved my boy toys. When I could wrestle them out of Dad's hands, that is.

It's little surprise then that I found more boyish pursuits to keep me entertained. And the best mud pies could be made at the end of the back garden under the apple trees. For hours I'd lose myself in an imaginary world of mud people, castles and heroines. Anyone looking on would see only a gloopy mess. People often say that when they gaze at the sky they can see animals, faces and story lines unfolding in the shapes and movements of the clouds; for me it was like that with mud.

My mother would ask me to help her bake, which I viewed as a cleaner version of playing with mud, though I was loath to wash my hands. She'd give me some dough in a separate bowl, which would be kneaded with my beloved mud and the odd blade of grass.

"Show it to Dad, he'll love it," she'd tell me, and I'd proudly present my culinary endeavours to him with little bits of stone and grass embedded in them. I guess that was her payback for him encouraging me to be a tomboy. But it was also a prelude to what would become one of my fondest childhood memories.

"Siobhán! Brian's at the door for you."

The boy next door.

"My mummy sent me in to play with you," he said by way of explanation as to why he was standing in my back garden wearing his Crimplene shorts and T-bar shoes.

Sure that he'd tease me, I blocked his view of my mud empire. But it turned out he liked mud too. We were both loners. Quickly, we decided we were the only two normal people on our road. Our relationship and view of the world lasted throughout our childhood and beyond. We had our own language and laughed at things other people couldn't see the humour in. As we progressed into our teens, we became versions of *Wayne's World* and *Dumb and Dumber*.

It was one of those summers that, in your mind's eye, went on forever and was filled with lazy sunny days. Back in a time when I had time to get bored. Life was slower and the depths of my decisions were whether to have a Vesta curry or a pouch of Smash for lunch. Those were the days when I could eat an entire packet of Mikado biscuits and still disappear if I turned sideways.

It was on one of those days that Brian called in and started mooching for food in the presses.

"There's nothing there," I said, as he opened the door of the press where the goody stash should have been.

"Your house always has something nice to eat. Your dad can't resist buying chocolate."

"He's a diabetic now – Mum won't let him."

"Where's his secret hiding place then?"

"Down the side of his Parker Knoll, but it's no use. I've already checked and there's just empty wrappers."

"Has your mum not been to the supermarket then?"

I shook my head. "Not until Friday. Yours?"

"No. It's not right, you know. Don't they know we're off school? The least they can do is make sure we don't starve to death!"

I nodded in agreement. What were parents coming to?

"There's custard powder and jelly cubes," I said.

"Do you know how to make them?"

I shrugged. "It can't be that hard if my sister can do it."

I took the packs from the cupboard and we set to work. Our first attempts were gelatine blobs, but it tasted okay so we ate them anyway. Brian got fed up waiting for the jelly to set so when he flipped it out of the bowl it spread like a jellyfish on Dollymount Strand. He tried spooning the remaining custard on top of it. We surveyed our work.

"It looks like an alien," I said.

"Or a custard beastie . . ."

We looked at each other, grinning, before wordlessly hunting down wizened old carrots from the bottom of the vegetable drawer. Our creative genius set to work – the Custard Beastie was born.

Brian and I wangled extra supplies of custard and jelly from our parents, who could have sworn they just bought it last week. We assured them they hadn't.

Custard Beasties began to appear on letterboxes, park benches and gate pillars around the greater Raheny area. Lime-green, red and blackberry-flavoured jelly formed the base. We used food colour to dye the custard various shades, sometimes we'd end up with a tie-dye effect that was rather artistic, or so we liked to think. Dead bluebottles were gathered from windowsills and encased in the moulds.

The real finishing touch came with the added accessories. Nothing was safe – my mother's false eyelashes, my sister's striped Bay City Rollers socks. Brian tried to borrow his grandmother's dentures but inconveniently she'd woken up.

Now, I should say our Beasties came to this earth with a message for humankind. We attached notes to them with cocktail sticks. From *"You've been beastied!"* to *"Beware! The Beasties are coming!"* or *"Attack of the Beasties!"*

On some level we hoped to start a kind of HG Wells *War of the Worlds* reaction. The Beasties would usually appear after dark, thanks to our agility and ability to climb out windows. Strangely, our Beasties failed to make the pages of the *Northside People*. Our supplies dried up and our desire to make our Beasties famous didn't extend as far as spending our pocket money on jelly and custard powder, and mud just didn't have the same effect.

I was sitting on the wall one night with Brian. My parents were out to dinner and my sister was in charge. She was in the back room listening to Neil Young and blowing smoke out the window.

"I'm bored," he said. "We should liven this road up."

"How?" I asked.

He shrugged. "Nic Nak?"

I tutted. "That's for kids." After a moment's silence, I continued. "My dad told me when he was a boy he used to tie a piece of thread from a lamppost to a bush. It was so thin you couldn't see it but it could knock a man's hat back off his head."

"We could try it with old fella Murphy when he comes home from the pub. What time is it?"

"How would I know?"

"Have you even got any thread?"

I threw him a withering look, silently slipping off the wall. I returned with an industrial-size cob of thread. You have those lying around the house when the family business is a sewing factory.

"Cool. How much is on it?"

"Fifty thousand feet."

"That should do it."

We tied thread from tree to tree and from streetlight to pillar. We'd watch unsuspecting walkers as they swatted what they thought was a gnat nipping at them. But the best was when Mr Murphy came swaying up the road.

For years, he had subjected his neighbours to visits on his way home from the local. It started off as a friendly "Just dropping in to say hello. Whiskey, did you say? Ah, sure, I'll just have a drop," but progressed to my mum having to forcibly close the hall door on him as he attempted to gain entry to our house, and drinks cabinet. By day, Mr Murphy was the most respectable-looking man of the estate. He wore a shirt and tie even though he was retired and a brown tweed jacket with patches on the elbows. Yet by evening a different beast emerged (not of the custard type either). One afternoon he stopped me on the road with a message for me to pass on to my mother and father. I stood solemnly nodding as he ripped shreds from their character, painting them to be Judases that were no longer welcome in his home. He didn't use foul language, and was eloquently spoken, albeit slurred. I ran home, eyes stinging from the insults and whiskey fumes that tumbled out of him. My parents dismissed it – the tirade was sparked by my mother telling him, whilst he was sober, that he was not to knock on our door drunk again. My father was hurt though, I could see it in his eyes. A non-drinker himself, he'd been very tolerant of Mr Murphy's invasions.

So that night when Old Man Murphy came swaying up the road after ten too many, vengeance for the family honour was mine. Okay, so thread-pinging isn't exactly on the level of a horse's head in the bed but it wasn't bad considering my age, limited resources and animal-loving nature. It was with great satisfaction I watched as Murphy flinched, walked on, slapped his face, waved his arms until as the thread became denser his arms and legs flayed in random motion as though he were being controlled by an invisible and mad puppeteer. Watching from the safety of an upstairs bedroom, the sight was as sweet as a summer stick of rock from West Cork.

Brian's older brother was walking behind Murphy. A Mod in a long black coat and Doc Martens, Karl rarely broke into a smile, not in front of his kid brother and his dorky friend, that is. I thought Karl was the most handsome boy on the planet. He cocked his thumb as he came in, a grin on his face.

"I've just seen old fella Murphy trying to do a break dance all the way up the street!"

Proudly, we let him in on our secret. Instead of being impressed and seeing me in a whole new light, he said we weren't thinking big or bold enough. He asked for the cob of thread and told us to follow him. We watched as he ran the thread from pole to pole across the road. I wasn't sure what he was playing at. I mean, thread wouldn't affect a car. Still Karl walked from pole to pole until the thread was no more. Looking back I realise our road must have been very quiet, but then Ireland in the seventies was a different place, and not every household owned a car. Still, we didn't have to wait long. A car approached, drove through the thread and then stopped. I was right. Thread was no match for a car. However, it did cause the wipers to fly up on the windscreen. Now, if I was writing fiction, this is the point my editor would challenge me, but what can I say – that's what happened. The driver, a neighbour in her early twenties, drove on after a few moments to her family home a few doors up. Within minutes her mother, wearing slippers and chenille dressing gown appeared. We ran for cover but we hadn't moved quickly enough to hide the evidence. From the house we could see her inspecting the trail of broken thread.

Next came the door banging.

"Come out here, you gurriers! I've been watching you all night! Open this door!"

No chance. Yet she kept banging.

"Our Yvonne thought she'd driven through a ghost the way her wipers moved. You're not going to get away with this! Siobhán McKenna, looking like butter wouldn't melt in your mouth – wait until your mother gets home!" *Bang, bang.*

I'm not sure which was more thrilling – being persecuted by Mrs Gunn in her fluffy nightclothes or colluding with the most handsome boy on the planet, who it appeared was seeing me for the first time. None of it lasted, of course. Karl got bored and went to play his LPs, not inviting us to join him. Mrs Gunn, who eventually gave up, lay in wait for my parents. When they pulled into the driveway, she was across the road quicker than a Mad March Hare.

"I'm going to get it now for letting you stay on the road," said my sister, rolling her eyes, but the admonishment never came.

My mum apologised but gave Mrs Gunn short shrift. Although Dad never said anything, I could have sworn there was a glint of pride in his eyes that his youngest daughter was keeping the tradition of his 1940s Cork city-centre practical pranks alive in modern Dublin suburbia.

My career as a practical joker spanned my entire childhood. From the mud pies, to the first whoopee cushion Dad bought me from Hector Grey's discount stall on Moore Street, to Custard Beasties – right up until I did my Leaving Cert at sixteen where in school I was more interested in being a master itching-powder purveyor, plastic-spider placer and, yes, if I'm being honest, placing wind-inducing power in the canteen soup, than I was in my French grades.

If I was a child again, I'd recapture the innocence and laughter of those practical jokes that never really did anyone harm. Perhaps we helped a drunken man to consider cutting back on his scoops the following night. And maybe the young driver might have slowed down and not be so quick to declare seeing a ghost again. So really in a way Brian and myself were providing a community service . . . though as I said, I'm not sure everyone shared our childhood view of the world.

Siobhán McKenna is a best-selling contemporary fiction novelist, short-listed for an Irish Book Award, and winner of Poolbeg/TV3's Write a Bestseller competition 2011. Through her affiliation and training with Deepak Chopra MD, she is currently writing her first non-fiction work. She lives on the Dublin coast with her family, rescue dogs, and a variety of wildlife, which includes foxes, red squirrels, hawks and a wandering peacock.

Play It Again, Sam

Roisin Meaney

I don't remember much about my childhood – it happened too long ago. If I try to think back that far, mostly what I get are snatches of isolated incidents: a raggedy chorus being sung by the assorted occupants of the back seat of a car on the way to some holiday or other; sinking in mud up to the tops of my white ankle socks at the edge of some lake; sliding down a haystack in a field in County Clare (cue one angry farmer); a tabby cat being wheeled around in the giant pram we all served time in; one of my brothers looking green around the gills after drinking paraffin that had been stored in a lemonade bottle. The usual kind of thing.

In general, I'm fairly sure my childhood comprised the usual mix of juvenile traumas, adventures, discoveries, triumphs and near-disasters that I imagine most children experience – a best-of-times, worst-of-times kind of upbringing. We muddled along together as siblings do, we fell out and made up and fell out again on a pretty regular basis, and nobody got seriously injured in the process.

But let me rummage around a little more thoroughly in my head and pull out what tatty remnants of my early years lurk there, in order to decide how I might relive a day as a child, if I ever got the chance.

I can declare with some certainty that I was the third-born in a good Irish Catholic seven-child family, slotted between an older and a younger brother. I was the second, and definitely the less scholarly, of two girls (my sister was an exemplary student – our mutual teachers couldn't believe we were related).

It's depressingly evident from photos of the time that I was not a good-looking child. In my defence, I would like to make it clear that this wasn't entirely my fault. Until I was about ten my mother sent me to the barber, along with my five brothers, to get my hair cut. The barber lived five or six doors away from us, and carried out after-hour operations in his own home (and probably gave my mother some kind of a group discount – six for the price of five, maybe). No allowance was made for the fact that I was, in fact, female. My crew cut was identical to my brothers', complete with the buzzer-up-the-back-of-the-head manoeuvre to finish it off. For some reason my sister was spared this ignominy, and floated through her (swotty) childhood with long girly hair.

Thankfully, I was eventually deemed too old to be sent to a male-oriented hairdresser – but rather than this leading to an improvement in my appearance, things went from bad to decidedly worse. My mother got it into her head that she could easily fulfil the role of my hair stylist: all she needed was a kitchen scissors, a sheet of newspaper, a towel – and a pudding bowl. Cross my heart. I must have been the most obliging and compliant child ever.

In addition, I had the sweet tooth that seemed a mandatory characteristic of the members of my generation. At every opportunity I sucked bulls' eyes and gobstoppers, chewed penny toffees, devoured sherbet sticks – you name it, I ate it. Inevitably, I was punished for my inveterate munching and crunching with a visit to the dentist, who took one look at the sorry state of affairs inside my mouth and declared that several teeth would have to be removed, before they contaminated the few decent ones I had left.

Thankfully they were my milk teeth, and were replaced before long with more grown-up versions, most of which I've managed to hang on to, but the memory of having a cotton-wool mask laid on my face and soaked with ether, and being held down by at least four adults as I thrashed and roared in an effort to draw a breath, remains as terrifyingly vivid today as it was then.

Add to the homemade hairstyle and gummy appearance the fact that I wore glasses from the age of about six, the ones they handed out free to the less affluent short-sighted kids among us, and you have some idea of how photogenic a child I made.

Notwithstanding my gawkish appearance, or maybe in an effort to compensate for it, my parents decided to send me to piano lessons at around eight years of age. Mrs O'Malley lived up the road (in the opposite direction to the barber) and taught piano to various schoolchildren. I was duly enrolled, and began my tuition.

To the best of my recollection, I lasted six weeks. I hadn't a musical bone in my body – or if I did, it was well hidden behind whatever else was inside there. I detested having to practise, and did so with a very bad grace. I nearly took the sitting-room door off its hinges every time I went in for the obligatory half hour. I would sit at the piano and plink and plonk joylessly until I was allowed to come out.

In vain, poor Mrs O'Malley battled to instil a love of music in me. Week after week I continued to learn nothing at all, and eventually it was agreed all round that the money being spent on the lessons could be put to far better use. (Needless to say, my sister took to the piano immediately, and played beautifully for years. Maybe the long hair helped.)

Ironically, I would dearly love to be able to play the piano, or any instrument, now, but I figure that the old-dog-new-tricks principle probably applies, and I'm afraid to try taking up an instrument again in case I fail miserably for the second time.

To be honest, I'm not altogether sure I would wish to relive my childhood. Since hitting adulthood I've always been a big fan of children, and enjoy their company enormously, but to go back myself and do it all again isn't something that fills me with eagerness.

If I only had to do it for twenty-four hours though, if I had just one day to fill as my childish self – and if it could be slotted somehow into my actual childhood, so whatever I did during that day would impact on all that came after it – here's how I'd spend it.

Assuming money was no object (and this is fantasy, so let's give me an unlimited budget here) I would start with an appointment at a top hair salon. I would demand the most accomplished stylist and place myself in his or her hands, and hope for the best. Maybe if I got one decent cut, it would make my mother realise that her younger daughter deserved better than Bob the Barber (not his real name!) or her good self as my coiffeur.

Hair sorted, I'd move on to my next appointment. I'd knock on Mrs O'Malley's door and present myself for my first piano lesson – and this time I'd pay attention, and listen to the instruction, and move my fingers as directed. I'd do my best to take in all that the good woman was saying, in the hope that if I started on the right note (oops) I might find the motivation to carry on, and possibly even get to the stage, many months or years hence, where I could sit at a piano and produce sounds that I, and others, would actually want to hear.

After leaving Mrs O'Malley's house I'd visit the chemist and invest in a new toothbrush, giving the sweet shop a wide berth on the way. Knowing now what I know about the horrors of ether, I'd do my damndest to keep away from the toffees and the liquorice allsorts and switch to apples and oranges and the like, and a swanky new toothbrush just might encourage me in my quest for healthier gnashers.

And finally, I'm not sure if contact lenses had been invented when I was small – I didn't come into possession of a pair until years later – but I'd hunt around, and if they were to be got I'd invest in a pair, and throw the free specs into the nearest bin.

And then I'd go home and wait for the gasps of admiration before heading into the sitting room to do an hour of piano practice.

Despite having lived in Africa, London, Canada and San Francisco, Roisin Meaney is Irish through and through. In 1977 she entered a competition on the back of a cereal box and won a car. In 2001 she entered a Write a Bestseller competition and won a two-book publishing deal. Since then she's had nine adult novels and two children's books published, and she's made the Irish top five fiction list three times (with one number one). Her books have been translated into several languages and two have been published in the US and Canada. She currently lives with a cat in the West of Ireland. In her spare time she tells stories to tots in her local library, gives writing workshops to anyone who'll listen to her, and occasionally enjoys a pint of Guinness, washed down with a nice red wine.

Hey, Skinny

Helen Moorhouse

"Hey, Skinny! What are you doing inside here on a lovely day like today?"

"*I'm reading my book.*"

"Well, can't you do that outside? You're awful pasty. Go and get a bit of Vitamin D, you miserable thing – but make sure you put on a good slather of sunscreen."

"*But I'll never get a tan if I wear sunscreen! I've been trying to get a watch-mark on my arm . . . but I just get bored sunbathing.*"

"It's not your natural habitat."

"*There's nothing to do except lie there and, anyway, it's a total waste of time – no matter how burned I get, it never turns a proper brown. I don't think I'm trying hard enough.*"

"You're trying too hard. The fact of the matter is that no matter how red you get, you'll never, ever, in a million years turn any shade of brown. All you'll do is feel pain."

"*But if I don't get a tan I'm all purple, and corned-beefy – no one will ever fancy me looking like that.*"

"Trust me, no one will fancy you looking like a radioactive raspberry. And the blistering and the peeling ain't pretty either."

"*But once you've peeled, isn't the tan underneath? I was going to use some baby oil to get as burnt as possible – that'll do the trick . . .*"

"No, you bloody moron! Haven't you even heard of skin cancer in 1984? You're fair-skinned. People who get tans aren't. Factor 50. Go on, that's it. Wear sunscreen. There's even a song about it . . ."

"*Who the hell are you and how did you get in here anyway?*"

"Tell you later. What are you reading?"

"*It's about a girl who had a really hard life and had a cruel stepmother who told her she was going nowhere and how she'd never amount to anything and she meets this really wealthy businessman's son and they fall head over heels but she gets pregnant and has to run away and –*"

"She thinks she'll never see the love of her life again and she faces all sorts of adversity and yet she overcomes the odds and meets up with yer man totally by chance and they live happily ever after, especially seeing as how the wicked stepmother was crushed under a collapsed slag heap?"

"*Ah here, don't ruin the ending – have you read it?*"

"Well, clearly I have but . . . never mind. I thought you liked horror stories? Stephen King and stuff?"

"*Well, I do, but everyone will think I'm a weirdo if I read those. Anyway, you learn stuff from the women in these books.*"

"Like what, exactly?"

"*Like how to be tough. How to be sharp and cut people down with a single line and then they respect you.*"

"It doesn't work like that."

"*It does. I think girls who can do that are great – it shows they can really stand up for themselves once they put people down. They always seem to get exactly what they want.*"

"Did you get all that from bodice-rippers?"

"*And on TV and in the movies. No one messes with them.*"

"Putting someone down isn't all it's cracked up to be, Pointy Ribs."

"*So why are you calling me names?*"

"Because it's a very difficult habit to kick once you start. You're not enjoying being on the receiving end of it, though, are you?"

"No."

"And does it make you like me?"

"No."

"And does it make you respect me?"

"*It's annoying me.*"

"See. Told you."

"*Anyway, she finally meets back up with this guy and she's a self-made success and wears lovely peach suits and white shoes and has a gorgeous perm and he falls in love with her and they get this second chance at love really late in life . . .*"

"Peach, you say. Nice. How late is really late?"

"*Nearly thirty, I think . . .*"

"That's not so late."

"*Not too late, I suppose – but by then most people are married ages. I'll probably have teenage kids by then and all that jazz.*"

"I wouldn't bet on it."

"*What did you say?*"

"Look – stick to the horror. It'll stand to you."

"*What do you mean by that?*"

"Just trust me."

"*So you reckon that you don't have to be hard as nails to get places?*"

"Look, it's the eighties – of course, you think that you have be a tough girl to succeed but it won't be all Thatcher and terrible shoulder pads forever."

"*What's terrible about shoulder pads? Fergie and Princess Di wear them all the time!*"

"Precisely. Besides, you're not a shoulder-pads kind of person."

"*So I'm not a sunbathing or a shoulder-pads person? You seem to know an awful lot about me?*"

"Cool your jets. I'm just older than you. What do you want to do with your life then?"

"Be an author. Write books. It probably won't work out though . . ."

"It might."

"What? Sorry, I didn't hear you?"

"Nothing. What else?"

"Emmm, get married, I suppose. To someone like Tom Cruise . . ."

"You'll change your mind on that one, trust me."

". . . who makes loads of money and I suppose we'll get a house with four or five bedrooms. It'll all get boring though when I get to about forty and it's just same thing, different day."

"Wow! You have a pretty sucky attitude."

"Look, no offence, but why do you keep putting me down?"

"Firstly, don't start a sentence with 'no offence'. It actually means the complete opposite and it's horribly passive-aggressive. Secondly, I'm not putting you down – why are you so sure that life gets stale at forty?"

"Well, it's all over by then, isn't it? Your kids have left home and it's just you and your husband . . ."

"Tom Cruise, right?"

"Well, hopefully – although knowing my luck I'll get Rowan Atkinson or somebody . . ."

"Don't judge books by covers. Anyway, you *could* hit a total jackpot. You shouldn't think so negatively, you know."

"Well, according to you I'm not going to get anywhere in life."

"I didn't say that. I said you weren't going to get anywhere with a put-on 'I'm a tough broad' attitude when clearly you're not."

"Wow. Thanks for the vote of confidence."

"Lots of people are good at tough but there's actually nothing wrong if you're not. It's being true is what matters. It's being yourself."

"I can't do that! Who wants a wimp who gets bored sunbathing? Who can't keep her room tidy? Who cries if she's away from home? Who's all swotty and wears knitted Fair Isle jumpers and Clarks shoes?"

"Well, some things never change. But look on the bright side – you won't always be scrawny!"

"*What? How do you know all this? Oh my God, are you* me? *Have you been sent from the future or something?*"

"Keep your voice down. Something like that."

"*You're* me! *Actually* me . . . *and you're right – clearly I'm* not *always going to be scrawny.*"

"Touché."

"*So* what happens to me? *How old are you? When have you come from?*"

"I'm really old by your standards but not by most people's. And I can't tell you exactly what happens but I can tell you that I'm from a time when you're happy."

"*Is that it? Happy? Not a world-famous actress winning Oscars or a big-time Hollywood director?*"

"I thought you wanted to be a writer."

"*I can always change my mind. Can you tell me more about this 'happy'? Doesn't sound amazing.*"

"Like you say – you can always change your mind. It all depends on where you set the bar."

"*So am I just ordinary?*"

"Don't sound so disappointed."

"*I just thought . . . it's going to be alright, though, is it? Everything is just going to plod along as normal until I get to fifty or whatever? Nothing really bad is going to happen?*"

"I can't guarantee that. Really bad stuff happens to a lot of people. You'll get through."

"*I'll get through? That doesn't sound great? What the hell is going to happen?*"

"I can't tell you specifics. And I don't know the whole future, just what's happened up until now."

"*So, like up to fifty?*"

"I'm not fifty! I come from when you're forty, okay? So I only know what's happened up until then."

"*Forty.*"

"Yes."

"*That's a bit scary.*"

"Try getting here. Ah, it's not bad – trust me."

"*You keep saying that. Why can't you tell me more? Like, do I become something I want to? Do I get married? Do I have kids? Am I rich?*"

"I can't tell you all that. All I can tell you is that I come from . . . a summer when you'll be driving along in your car . . ."

"*A Ferrari? Like Magnum PI?*"

"No . . ."

"*Do we all drive kind of space cars? Hovercraft? Wow – what's the future like? Is everything totally different, like with the government and stuff?*"

"Not entirely . . . anyway . . . you'll be driving along in your car and the trees will be so green and the sun so bright and you'll feel a moment of . . . well . . . contentment. With everything."

"*That's it?*"

"Well, it's a pretty big deal."

"*To you maybe – I think I'd like a bit more in my life than just one moment of contentment. Are you serious? Is everyone miserable in the future? Is everyone poor and it rains all the time?*"

"Emmmm . . ."

"*Oh my God, it is?*"

"No . . . look, I can't tell you specifics but there are things I need to say to you."

"*Life is going to be desperate, isn't it? It's going to be . . . like . . . this terrible ruined planet! Is there going to be a nuclear war? I'm not going to succeed at anything, am I? I'm never going to be good enough . . .*"

"Stop worrying. Being happy – content – is fantastic. Stop doubting yourself – but try to stay humble. And count your blessings – that's important."

"*What blessings? Like a crust of bread and no nuclear holocaust?*"

"Among other things. Always keep learning too. Absorbing stuff, watching stuff. Keep doing the things that you like, that you're good at. But that doesn't mean you don't try at stuff like maths."

"But I'm so bad at maths!"

"I know. You don't get better. Look – don't sweat too much about stuff like theorems . . ."

"Like what?"

"You'll find out soon enough. You do need to pay attention to problem-solving though. You'll have to do a lot of that."

"Great."

"Sarcasm. That's good. Just not too much, and not too nasty. Don't try to be someone you're not – just stay true to yourself. Be kind, be considerate, be thoughtful – if you can't say something nice then don't say it at all – or at *least* try to keep your voice down. Tell the truth. Try new things. Don't get a big head. Sort out problems when they're small – they have a habit of getting bigger if you ignore them and hope they'll go away. And do it with a smile. Work hard. Ignore nasties. Try to gravitate toward nice people. There are a lot of them about. Kind and good people who are on your side. Value your friends. Things happen for a reason and most of the time they can work out fine."

"That's a lot to remember. And none of it sounds very cool."

"It is cool. You are luckier than most. There will be times when you won't feel it but you are. Look – your future's so bright you're gonna have to wear shades."

"That's a good line."

"Glad I can still speak eighties. And . . . em. . . don't stop believing – there's a song about that too."

"I think I know it."

"That's it for now. That should cover us till we get to forty – and possibly beyond, but I don't know any more than that. I'm just keeping everything crossed."

"I will too then. But so far so good, eh?"

"Yeah, Skinny. So far so good."

Helen Moorhouse is originally from Mountmellick, County Laois and lives in Dublin with her husband and two daughters. She is a full-time novelist, speechwriter, copywriter and regular contributor to the *Irish Independent*. Her third novel, *Sing Me To Sleep*, was published in 2013 and is, along with her previous novels, *The Dead Summer* and *The Dark Water*, available from Poolbeg Press.

Stop and Smell the Roses

Sinead Moriarty

If I was a child again I'd be in less of a hurry to grow up. I wouldn't wish my life away. I was always waiting to be eighteen so I could leave school and go out into the "big bad world" and discover what life was really about.

I longed to shed my school uniform and wear my own clothes. I wanted to spread my wings and fly. Dublin was too parochial, Ireland was too small. I was going to head off and discover exotic places and far-flung lands.

I was far too impatient to shake off my childhood. In my naïveté I thought being a kid was no fun. Being an adult was so much better! When you were an adult people treated you as an equal. You could earn your own money and buy your own house and clothes and furniture and be independent. That's what I wanted.

I can see my own children's impatience to grow up and I wish I could stem it. I wish they'd stop longing for adulthood.

My seven-year-old son recently sighed and said, "I can't wait to be a grown-up."

"Why?" I asked.

"Because then I can do what I want."

"What is it you want to do?" I enquired, presuming he'd say be a fireman or a footballer or some such. How wrong I was . . .

"I want to buy a humongous TV and eat Nutella sandwiches all day," he said, eyes misting over at the thought of the blissful days he would spend flat on his back eating chocolate spread.

These are not the kind of dizzy heights I'd hoped he'd aim for, but it reminded me of how all children can't wait to grow up.

I didn't want to burst his bubble so I said nothing. I didn't tell him of the job he'd have to get to pay for the big TV. I didn't mention the money he'd have to save to have time off to watch the giant screen and eat Nutella sandwiches.

I didn't tell him of the dole queues and the ever-rising unemployment figures. I didn't mention that inflation has gone up, that trade surplus is down, that the GDP has fallen. I omitted to talk about bail-outs and banking crises.

Nor did I tell him that when times were good we partied like it was 1999 and forgot to save for a rainy day. And when the rains came, they were monsoons.

I didn't tell him that where once America was the Holy Land for Irish youths, it is now crippled by its own recession. I decided not to explain global economic meltdown, defaulting on mortgages or the spate of suicides amongst middle-aged Irish men with huge debts. Who said growing up was fun?

That's what I miss most about being young: the innocence. That's why we all must try to protect our children, and shield them from the difficulties of "real" life. It is up to us to preserve their sweet naïveté for as long as we can. Why be in a rush to grow up? It brings with it so much responsibility and so many complications.

I want to shout out to all children: "Stay young for as long as you can! Be a kid, be goofy and silly and foolish and carefree for as many years as possible. You'll never get the time back. Enjoy it, embrace it and have fun. Laugh until your stomach aches, climb trees, put on plays, make forts, sleep in the garden in a tent, roll down grassy hills, splash in muddy puddles . . . be happy."

If I was a child again I would choose the same friends. I was lucky, I chose well. Children need to choose their friends wisely. When you're a child you should feel good about yourself when you're with your friends, not bad. Your friends should make you feel comfortable and not ill at ease.

Don't waste any time trying to be in with the "cool" gang. It's not worth it, you'll never fit in. Be with like-minded people. Spend time with other kids who have the same interests as you, kids you can be yourself with, kids who are loyal and trustworthy friends.

A child can't know it, but friends are a vital part of life. In thirty years' time, that kid you sat beside in Biology may be the very person whose shoulder you cry on when your life is in tatters. That person could be someone who helps you when you're down, supports you when you need it most and cheers you on when things go well. That person will be someone who will stand by you through thick and thin. Good friends are the invaluable treasures of life.

I wish I'd known back then that I would become a writer. It would have been wonderful to know that those English essays I slaved over would stand to me in later years as I wrote novels. If only I'd known those essays were to be my apprenticeship for future books!

I definitely would have worked harder and concentrated more in typing class if I'd known how many hours, days, weeks, months and years I'd spend typing words in the future.

If I was a child again I wouldn't worry so much about what people thought of me. I wouldn't try to please everyone so much. I would understand that teachers are human beings with complicated lives. I'd realise that they have bad days and when they snap at you for no apparent reason that it isn't personal, they're just stressed.

I'd also understand that exams, while important, are not the be-all and end-all of life. I would worry so much less about results and grades. I'd know that it takes a long time for most people to figure out what they want to do with their lives and that lots of people never do.

I'd realise that finding the right career can be a slow process and that sometimes it's a process of elimination. You have to try different things until you find the right fit. I'd love to have known that I'd be one of those lucky people who manages to turn their hobby into a job. I would have fretted so much less about college and career options.

If I was a child again I'd know that boys are shyer and more awkward than girls. I wouldn't believe those kids who boasted about "going all the way". The kids who made you feel so inadequate for not even having got to "second base". I'd know they were lying and I wouldn't feel so useless.

I would dance like no one was watching instead of being so self-conscious all the time. I'd talk to boys I liked instead of running away from them because I could never think of anything to say. I wouldn't waste time on boyfriends who drank too much or flirted with other girls or didn't ring when they said they would.

I'd know that boys like girls who make them laugh. They like girls who listen and are kind, girls who can hold their own in a discussion and girls who have their own lives and don't depend on them for everything. I'd know that one day I'd meet someone who "got me" and that I'd be lucky enough to marry him.

If I was a child again, I would worry so much less about being pale-skinned. Instead of burning my skin to fire-engine red every summer, I'd sit in the shade. I'd understand that roasting yourself alive every time the sun poked its head out from behind a cloud was not a good idea. I would refrain from putting oil on my skin in order to "get a better tan". I would know that a tan was something that I would never achieve, no matter how hard I tried, no matter how many times I burnt myself. Instead of thinking that red was better than white, I'd have the sense to protect my skin from the ravages of sun damage. I would have avoided years of heat rash, blisters and peeling. A big sunhat would have been my best friend instead of a bottle of Johnson's Baby Oil lathered on to my alabaster skin.

If I was a child again, I would embrace my Irishness and not be ashamed of it. I would be proud of my heritage and understand that wherever I went in the world, people would smile warmly when I said I was Irish. I'd know that this small island on the edge of Europe is known globally as a wonderful place to live. I'd realise that it wasn't just U2 that made my country "cool". I would know that talent lay in every corner of this land and that Irish writers, poets and musicians were lauded and feted around the world.

If I was a child again I'd know how lucky I am to be born in this era, in this country. I'd rejoice in my heritage, my culture and most of all in my good fortune to have been given the greatest gift of all: a happy childhood.

Sinead Moriarty was born and raised in Dublin, where she grew up surrounded by books. Her mother is an author of children's books. Growing up, she was inspired by watching her mother writing at the kitchen table and then being published. From then on, her childhood dream was to write a novel. She wrote her first book *The Baby Trail* while working as a journalist in London. She is published by Penguin and has, to date, written nine novels. They have been widely translated.

Running with the Wild Bunch

Eugene O'Brien

I had a very fortunate, happy childhood. Let me say that up front. We were loved and felt safe and were afforded great opportunity which a lot of children were not. But on the last day of sixth class, running around the playground of St Joseph's National School, Edenderry, County Offaly, although feeling happy and excited and carefree, there was the first twinge of a butterfly in my tummy. Something loomed on the horizon. Something that would have to be faced. I tried to put it out of my head. There was the whole summer to look forward to but I knew, no matter what, that time runs out, and that life would change. I was to start boarding school.

My grandfather had gone there, and his brothers, and my father and his brothers, and my mother's father, but still I could not deny the panic in my heart when my parents drove away that first day after dropping me off at my new school. I was shown to my dormitory, I put up my Man U posters and tried to envisage my new surroundings as home, but it was useless.

It was September 1979, I was eleven going on twelve and was about to break a family tradition. I was running away from boarding school. Not the school's fault: good teachers, grand group of lads. If you could ignore the obsession with rugby, and a slight whiff of entitlement, it was pretty okay, but I just knew that the whole boarding gig was not for me. The upper lines, the lower lines, bad food, first year being called "Rudiments", life ruled by timetables and the constant presence of a peer group, night and day – no escaping from it at 4 p.m. All of the above and, of course, missing home and family, caused an uncontrollable urge to start walking out the front gates and onto the road. A kind of dream state took over and I was in another world, a world of uncertainty, an adventure, like a movie. I was breaking one family tradition, and kept thinking of another.

The local cinema was bought by my grandfather in the 1950s. Situated in the town square, it was the place where I'd spent every childhood Saturday at matinees. We were served up Disney and other kids' flicks but also adult fare like the spaghetti westerns. We were upset when John Wayne was butchered by Bruce Dern in *The Cowboys*. We were Kung Fu experts after seeing Bruce Lee, practising our moves afterwards, high on minerals and Captain Hurricane bars.

But the abiding image, and one that came back to me on the road home that evening was the opening images of *The Wild Bunch*. A group of children torture a scorpion in a nest of red ants, eventually setting it on fire, intercut with the Wild Bunch riding into town, the screen freezing on each member as their names popped up on the screen . . . William Holden, Ernest Borgnine *et al*. I saw the movie when I was nine or ten and the kids had always haunted me.

Walking along the road I started to trot as on a horse. I was the Wild Bunch, trying to decide whether to chance thumbing a lift, aware that the light was fading, and wondering what kind of reception I would receive at home. I'd just explain how I felt and hope that my parents would understand. Reality was beginning to kick in because of hunger and thirst, and the movie world that had been a distraction was fading.

Then I passed a hedge in front of a bungalow with a man clipping away at it with shears. We nodded at each other and then he addressed me, saying that he'd passed me on the road earlier and asking if I had been walking for long. Not long, I replied, going into some yarn about visiting an aunt in Prosperous who had left me at the bus stop but I had missed the bus and she had gone out to play bridge, so I was making my own way home to Edenderry. He didn't buy this for a second but left the tale unchallenged, instead asking me in for refreshment. I checked behind him and saw a woman in the kitchen window looking out at us. He reassured me that it was okay, so I accepted the offer.

In their kitchen I drank 7Up – it tasted like no other mineral ever had – and they gave me soup, which I devoured. His wife enquired about where I was going, so I repeated the yarn. The man then told me he was a teacher and showed me a class of lads he had taught, and told me that one of them was a very famous sportsman – could I pick him out? I scanned the photo, glad that this question-of-sport session was a distraction from my made-up story of aunts and missed buses, and even more pleased when I recognised Eamonn Coghlan. Before the glory days of Jack's army, he vied with the show-jumpers as Ireland's number-one sporting hero.

The photo was put away as the man mentioned, out of the blue, the name of my boarding school and asked if I was aware of its existence, and he afforded himself a knowing smile just to let me know he knew where I was coming from.

They would drive me home. I mentioned the current oil strikes and how petrol was scarce but they insisted and half an hour later they dropped me outside my house. I thanked them profusely and I shook his hand, the kindness of strangers encouraging tears which were welling but not showing themselves until the car had moved on.

My parents were a little taken aback: I should have just rung them but I suppose, in a way, I had been more calculating than I'd realised. I had wanted to make a big impression on them. A statement.

I didn't start in the local school on Monday, as I'd planned.

On my parents' urging I did go back and give the boarding school another go, but by mid-November I was off again. This time I was better prepared, making the dash after lunch on a full stomach. I hitched two rides and was home by tea. As always, my parents were very understanding. The local headmaster was called and I couldn't wait to dash next door to my friend since High Infants, Kenneth, and give him the news that we'd be cycling to school together the following Monday.

The lads were very welcoming and although the school was old and rundown with prefabs out the back and an old stove heater in the classroom, with the occasional mouse making an appearance, I couldn't have been happier.

I sometimes wonder where that couple is now. Is he still teaching or retired by now? Do they still live in the same bungalow, and does he still trim his hedge on September evenings? I suppose he would be in his late sixties now, but that's only a guess, as is the location of their home, which was somewhere between Prosperous and Allenwood.

Eamonn Coghlan never won an Olympic medal but did us proud in 1983 in Helsinki, winning Gold in the world championships. The boarding school is still churning out captains of industry and rugby teams. The cinema closed in 1996, having battled against the 1980s video boom and a new multiplex in Tallaght. But the feelings it aroused in me and the stories my dad tells me of its heyday when people queued round the square to get in will stay with me, as will that feeling of walking on the road pretending to be the Wild Bunch and knowing somehow that I was doing the right thing.

Eugene O'Brien wrote the play *Eden*, first performed in the Abbey Theatre in 2001. It won the Stewart Parker award, the Rooney prize for literature and the *Irish Times*/ESB Award for best new play, and has been performed in many countries and London's West End. His second play *Savoy* debuted in the Peacock Theatre, Dublin, in 2004. He has written three plays for RTÉ radio drama: *The Nest*, *Sloth*, and *Numb* (nominated for the Writers' Guild Zebbie Award). He wrote the screenplay for the film *Eden*, which played at many festivals including New York's Tribeca festival (winning Best Actress for Eileen Walsh) and secured an American release with Liberation films. His critically acclaimed television series *Pure Mule* and the two-part follow-up *Pure Mule – The Last Weekend* were nominated for fourteen IFTAS.

My Cousin Jodie

Jennifer O'Connell

I am compelled by some unfortunate chink in my genes to record things. I've always done it, beginning with the diaries I kept from the day of my sixth birthday until the day of my nineteenth. I stopped writing them at roughly the sáme time I started recording things for a living. With all that practice under my belt, you'd think I'd be better at it.

But memory is strange, slippery territory – this memory in particular. It isn't even a memory, so much as a series of disconnected images, like one of the films my father recorded on his old cine camera. The tighter I try to hold onto it, the more it frustrates me. I want to remember, not for her, but for myself. Because of what happened later.

First, the background. It was the late 1970s. An Ireland of the Troubles and tightening our belts. An Ireland in which everything really did seem to exist in shades of brown.

My mother insists that I was a beautiful child. Documentary evidence of the time doesn't really bear this out: it records instead a solemn, round-faced baby who became a solemn, round-faced girl, observing the world from her pushchair with a faintly cynical frown.

I remember that pushchair – I ensconced myself in it shortly after my birth and refused to move until, sometime around my third birthday, my mother sat me on the fashionable orange-and-white rug in the hall and explained to me in no uncertain terms that it was time I learned to walk.

For now, my world still revolved around the buttercup-yellow Stanley in my granny's kitchen, the Quaker-run nursery school I attended with my impish, curly-haired big brother, and outings in my mother's Renault 4.

The strict set of rules that governed the life for a child of the 1970s had not yet made themselves known to me. Fun, at the convent school to which I would shortly graduate from the pushchair, was looked on as something faintly perilous; a laughing child was an incendiary device. There were rules about the kind of shoes you could wear (no patent; slippers in the classroom); rules about when you could sharpen your pencil; rules about who could sing in the school choir and who must mime; rules about when you could *dúl amach go dtí an leithreas*; rules about when you could *bí ag caint* or *bí ag rith* or just *bí*.

But for now, my world was small, safe and blissfully rule-free.

It was on one of those endless hot summers that nostalgia insists punctuated every Irish childhood at regular twelve-monthly intervals. We drove up in the old Renault 4, air billowing in through the hole in the front passenger seat, to my great-grandmother's house in Woolengrange. Even writing the name still gives me a little thrill of expectation.

She swept into my life in Uncle Phil's black Morris Minor, which was a sleek, curvy piece of machinery with a tan leather interior and a purr like a panther's.

I liked Uncle Phil. He was my granny's favourite brother and a priest, but he was not like any priest I had met before, or since. He wore glasses like Buddy Holly, he laughed often, he spoke to me like I was an adult and, later, when I could read them, wrote me proper letters on seminary notepaper.

My pushchair was parked under the big apple tree in the

garden as the Morris Minor glided up. I must have been expecting them. I'm sure I had been told about it in advance, but I remember the feeling of surprise as its doors sprang open and out of it emerged Uncle Phil with a man who looked like a film star – a man with startling blue eyes, black hair and a leather jacket.

They stood blinking in the sunlight and the door stayed open for a minute or two longer until finally she climbed out. A girl in a dress the colour of candyfloss, a bright slash of colour in the sepia-tinted world I inhabited. Her hair was the exact shade of yellow of the middle stripe in a Loop the Loop ice lolly.

We were cousins, though I couldn't fathom how, because I knew all of my cousins – I could already recite their names by heart – and we'd never met before. But I didn't want to question it. She was an unexpected gift I had no intention of returning.

She wore pink gingham. She was two years older than me and she came from Australia. She said it like it was a question. "Australia?" She was Jodie, the daughter of my granny's youngest brother, Gerard, the man with the film-star eyes.

We played in the back garden. We drank TK Lemonade and ate Afternoon Tea biscuits, Mikados and Coconut Creams. My granny produced a Battenberg cake, carefully unfolding the brown-paper bag to reveal the pink-and-yellow chequerboard squares encased in a thick layer of sickly sweet marzipan that seemed to swell in your mouth. The mark of a sophisticated foodstuff was that it tasted like nothing encountered in nature.

We all gazed at Jodie in wonder – or I did, anyway. She raced around the big, stone kitchen, a little blonde whirlwind, and stopped every so often to put a sticky hand on Uncle Phil's knee, leaving a glistening trace of sugar and marshmallow on the knee of his priest's smart black trousers as all the adults looked benignly on.

She liked animals. We played with toy horses that Uncle Phil had brought. I called mine Clippity Clop.

I don't remember saying goodbye. She climbed into Uncle

Phil's Morris Minor, and I sat back in the pushchair as they vanished down the hill.

There won't be a happy ending to this story. You know that already, don't you? It was nearly twenty-five years later before I next saw her face.

The autumn of 2002. I was working in my dream job, the editor of the features section on a national newspaper; getting paid to record things at last.

Jodie, though I didn't know this yet, had managed to fix herself up with precisely her dream job too – she had just left her PA position in a publishing company to set up her own mobile dog-washing business, Aussie Pooch. Jodie still loved animals – she had even become a vegetarian.

That summer, I had got engaged to my long-term boyfriend, and we had just returned from a holiday in Italy to plan our wedding there. Half a planet away in Australia, my twenty-nine-year-old cousin was making plans too, for a trip to Indonesia.

We had recently moved into a new house: a pleasingly symmetrical, pink brick Guinness-built house with white-painted sash windows, nasturtiums running riot in the garden, and a bright red door. The house looked like a bit of the English countryside in inner-city Dublin; it had cast-iron fireplaces, ceramic light fittings and, in some rooms, seven layers of carpet and lino. Every time we opened a newspaper, its value seemed to have doubled. Life was good.

Jodie, too, had just bought her first house, in the Southern Sydney suburb of Como, in a joint mortgage with her mum. Life was good for her too, really good. Right up until the moment when it was interrupted.

Another decade has passed now, and I'm writing this on my balcony in Sydney, her city, and looking across at her skyline. I have the strangest feeling that someone should have pressed her phone number into my hand before I got on the plane and told me to look her up. I like to imagine I would have, that I would have called up Aussie Pooch and said, "I don't know if you remember me, but we met once when we were very small . . ."

But we don't do, do we? We mean to, but we hesitate, and then the moment slips away, and there are children to be collected from school or football, work deadlines to be met, dinners to be cooked, gardens to be sat in, and now, of course, I'll never know whether I would have.

It's more than ten years now since that autumn day when I was sitting at my desk with a chicken-and-sweetcorn sandwich, and I opened the newspaper. The photograph was an older version of the Jodie I remembered in a pink dress, with a broad smile and the same blonde hair, taken alongside her friend, a friend whose name, I would learn, was Michelle. Shelly, they called her.

Bali, the headline roared. She was at the Sari nightclub at Kuta beach at eight minutes past eleven, on 12th October 2002. She must have heard the first blast in Paddy's Pub across the road but, if she did, she would have had only twenty seconds to react before the second bomb, right outside the Sari.

Jodie did regain consciousness despite the burns that covered almost her entire body. Afterwards, a British woman who sat by her stretcher until it was loaded onto a plane to Perth told how, when they finally got some painkillers for her, she wouldn't take them. She said: "Don't worry about me – the girl in the next bed – give them to her."

They flew her home, where she was treated in the Royal Hospital in Perth. The staff there noted her politeness, her "fragile smile". Jodie died three days later, in her mum's arms.

It had been years, but even without the name, I would have recognised her. There were traces of my grandmother in her face.

I have wondered whether to end it there, but it wouldn't be the whole story.

I call my mother and tell her I want to record my memories of Jodie. She is puzzled, and for a moment I can't understand why.

"Am I remembering it wrong?"

It is a hot day, and I am sweltering in my car outside a Cole's or a Woollies', and she sounds very far away. She is very far away.

"Well, no – or at least you remember it more clearly than me."

"Then what?"

"Well, you were just a baby. You can't have been more than two, because your great-grandmother was still alive. I remember you as eighteen months or so."

"Wasn't I three or four?"

"No, you were only a baby. You were on my lap and when you weren't you never left your pushchair." Her tone is gentle, certain.

"So I didn't play in the garden with her? We didn't run around the kitchen together?"

"No, you didn't. You couldn't have. Sorry."

"Was there Battenberg?"

"I don't know, sorry." She says it kindly, but it stings all the same.

So it turns out that none of this is true.

Well, not quite none of it – there was a trip to Ireland at some point in the 1970s but, if I was there, there is no way I could actually remember it.

I don't remember Jodie. Instead I have – like the character in that Alice Munro story – pilfered someone else's recollections, along with some old photos and some actual memories which may have had nothing to do with her: Uncle Phil, the pushchair, my grandmother's taste for cakes wrapped in marzipan.

I so much wanted Jodie to have been real to me, I made her real. This realisation is astonishing, embarrassing – though I hope not insulting to her – but in its own way, it is sad too; another, lesser version of the stab of loss I felt that autumn day in 2002, looking at her photograph on my desk.

It makes me wonder, too, about other things I think I remember; about the other fictions to which I stubbornly cling, the other narratives I have unknowingly wrought. But in the end, I don't suppose it really matters. My memories – even the ones painstakingly recorded in those leatherbound books – may be invented or stolen or crudely cobbled together, but to me they all pulse with truth.

And in the end, isn't all memory a reinvention of something? The way, as Munro said, that we keep telling ourselves our stories and telling other people a somewhat different version of them? I'm left feeling like her character, Fame, in *The Progress of Love*. "How hard it is for me to believe that I made that up. It seems so much the truth it is the truth."

Jennifer O'Connell is a columnist and feature writer with the *Irish Times*. She is a regular contributor to programmes on Today FM, Newstalk, RTÉ Radio and RTÉ Television. In the past, she worked as founding editor of *TheJournal.ie* and features editor of *The Sunday Business Post*. Her journalism has been published in *Image Magazine*, *Irish Tatler*, the *Irish Independent* and the *Evening Herald*. She has also worked as a television news reporter and was the series producer of a series of critically acclaimed documentaries made by Liberty Films for RTÉ. She normally lives in Dublin but is currently spending a year in Sydney with her husband James, and their two children, Rosa and Lúí.

The Forgotten Child

Andrew O'Connor

When I was a child I had the most remarkable woman in my life. Although we called her our great-aunt, she was actually a great-great-aunt, my grandfather's relative. Stepping into her house was like stepping back in time. Although the house had long since been updated with the necessities of modern living, the furniture, the ornaments, the ambiance was from a bygone era. There were chocolate boxes from as far back as the 1930s, used to keep letters in, and oil lamps that still glowed. There was a curious atlas that had none of the geography we were being taught in school. The atlas showed a strange-sounding Austro-Hungarian empire, and above it nestled something called the German Empire occupying the spot we were being taught was now West Germany and East Germany. Ireland was marked in the same red colour as the United Kingdom with curious-sounding names like King's County and Queen's County which couldn't be correct as the map on the wall in school gave these places the far more down-to-earth if less regal titles of Offaly and Laois. But the atlas, like most things in her house, was from the era that she had grown up in.

But it was her stories that were of most interest – and how she loved stories! She had dabbled in acting when she was younger and had even written and produced plays. Maybe some other life had been waiting for her, but the destiny she chose was to stay and manage the farm that she had lived on all her life and that she had inherited when her own parents died. She didn't marry and had no children, but was close to us, her extended family. When I was a child she would have been in her eighties and yet she was sharp and sprightly and could connect so well with children. I never realised just what a link she was to the past. A direct link to the nineteenth century. When she was born, Victoria was still on the throne. When the First World War began she was already seventeen years of age. And by the time the Second World War had started she was well into her forties. What she must have lived through and experienced! So much first-hand knowledge and personal stories revolving around these historic events. And so many questions I would love to ask her if I had the chance again.

The stories she did tell were fascinating. She had known people who had sailed and died on the *Titanic*. As a child I didn't realise just how unusual this was. There were always films and programmes on the television about the *Titanic*, so I just presumed everyone must have known somebody on the *Titanic* back then. She told of the heartbreak the sinking had left behind for the family she knew who had lost someone. How the man's mother would wander at night to the nearby sea and stare out, looking for her lost son.

She had been around for so long she knew all the stories about people's families in the locality, stretching back generations that nobody else could recall. One story she recounted was of the great-grandparents of the people who lived in a house in a quiet wooded area nearby. Back in the 1920s they were a normal family going about their daily business. Until the mother of the family went missing one day. Her children arrived home from school and found her gone. There were no clues as to where she was and when she didn't turn up as the days went by, panic set in. Her husband and the police organised extensive searches through the countryside and woods but they could find no sign of her.

Fear swept the locality that she had been a victim of malice and nobody would travel out after dark on their own, fearing a murderer was at large. As the weeks went by and the searches continued, the mystery deepened. It was then discovered that the woman was alive and well and had moved into the remote house of a man who lived some distance away. What's more, the man she had run off to had taken part in the searches for her. When their ruse was discovered, the woman had calmly returned to her family and took up where she had left off. She and her family returned to their normal life and nothing more was said about it. To our modern ears it sounds unbelievable but, as we know, people didn't talk about things back then except in whispered conversations and it was soon forgotten by everyone. Except for my great-aunt who told the story to us.

There were plenty of other stories of different families. Two neighbours who had not spoken for three generations and the discord had been going on for so long that neither could remember what the feud was about any more. But my great-aunt could remember. The row originated over land back in 1916, she informed us. Then there was the tale of the man who made a fool of the bishop's sister at a train station that resulted in dire consequences for him.

The tales of her own family and upbringing were lighter and full of colour. Stories of mountain climbs and picnics, fairs and theatres. A tranquil setting for a happy family.

She was one of three children and had two brothers and they had grown up with their parents on that farm in the beautiful countryside. One of her brothers had emigrated to America, the other had remained in Ireland. Like her, neither of her brothers married and all lived to a good age and lived happy lives.

My great-aunt had outlived her two brothers and when she did pass away that branch of the family ended with her.

This all came back to me recently when I was writing my new

novel, which is set in the Edwardian era. As I was researching those times it all seemed so far away that it was amazing to think this woman I knew so well as a child had been part of it. You wonder when you're writing something set in the past whether you are getting details right, regardless of how much research you do, and with her great love of writing and stories my great-aunt would have loved to be part of setting the correct scene for a novel.

And then, as I continued my research, I came across something that really proves that life is so much stranger than fiction. As part of my research I was looking up old censuses to garner information on the lifestyles of the time. Now with the census being available on line, the process has become simplified and so much quicker. I was looking up the 1911 census and, realising my great-aunt would be a young girl of fourteen at the time, I went to search for her and her family's details. As I had the address of her family farm it would be easy to look them up and find them. And, sure enough, there she was on the census, living with her parents and two older brothers. But as I studied the information of the household something jumped out at me. There weren't five people living in that house. The census showed six people living there. My great-aunt, her parents, the two older brothers, and a fourth child. A boy called Jack that the census said was twelve years old in 1911. This couldn't be right. There were only three children in the family. I knew it, we all knew it, it was a given. And yet here was the census telling me otherwise. I studied the details and there was no mistake. The parents were registered as having four children. His surname was the same.

I started asking my family were they aware in any way of this fourth child, Jack. But it was as much of a surprise to them as to me. They believed there had only been my great-aunt and two brothers in the family. It was like this child, Jack, had simply been written out of history. What is most curious is that my great-aunt spoke so much about her family and of her other two brothers. And yet Jack was never even hinted at, let alone spoken about.

The 1911 census stated that Jack was at school and that he

could read and write, and so there didn't appear to be any intellectual difficulty to be hidden away as was so often the case back then. A multitude of explanations went through my mind. The most obvious one was that this young life had been cut short in tragic circumstances. Perhaps the pain of what happened was simply too much for the family to deal with and they never mentioned it again, so that, even when my great-aunt was in her eighties and all the rest of her immediate family were deceased, this pact not to talk about it or acknowledge it held fast. Perhaps Jack had been a casualty of war. Between the First World War, War of Independence and the Civil War the next decade was ruthless in claiming the lives of millions of young men of his generation. But then don't families honour their war heros? Unless he wasn't considered a war hero because he had fought on the wrong side – we had been taught that the Civil War set brother against brother and created feuds that went to their graves. Could something like this have occurred within this family? It couldn't be something as simple as he had emigrated because the elder brother had gone to America and he was regularly talked about. I remember in my great-aunt's house there was a very old blessing in a portrait on the wall and her parents' and two brothers' names were engraved into the blessing along with her name. But there was no mention of Jack even here. What could have been the circumstances that left this child out of their family history and life?

And then it occurred to me that perhaps he didn't die young at all. Perhaps there had been a ferocious feud and he had simply moved away to a new life. Perhaps the bitterness of this falling-out led to the rest of his family not ever mentioning him again. Imagine if this fourth child did marry and did have children. And perhaps his descendants are alive and well today, unaware of his and their own background. Perhaps this branch of the family didn't die with my great-aunt at all and lives on through this forgotten son and brother. So many questions and the person, my great-aunt, who could answer them is long gone and chose never to talk about it.

I wonder, if I had the chance again, if I could garner some insight from her. Little did I know that, of all the stories she told, the most interesting and mysterious of all was the one so close to home.

Andrew O'Connor is the bestselling author of seven novels including *The House*, *Talk Show* and *Full Circle*. He is a graduate of NUI Maynooth and Trinity College Dublin. His latest book, *The Secrets of Armstrong House*, was published by Poolbeg Press in October 2013.

The B-Game is Okay Too

Brian O'Connor

The number is seared in my memory – 1051: almost exactly halfway between the sanctuary of 1100 and the disaster of 1000, a middle-of-the-road purgatory for an anxious, middle-of-the-road, thirteen-year-old schoolboy. A figure with the potential to determine the rest of my life, apparently.

In a randomly divided crop of sixty first-year youngfellas, there had been Christmas and Easter exams, the total marks of which would determine the concrete division of the crop into "A" and "B" classes for second year and beyond. Get into "A" and it would be honours all the way. But "B" was, well, it didn't bear thinking about.

Except there was nothing else to think about: to the extent that the summer holidays before going back were dominated by fear, and prayers that the class would be dull – not thick, but unexceptional, nothing to write home about, average, very, very average. That way the cut-off would be a thousand. And an ordinary 1051 would be enough. Except it wasn't.

The classes weren't called 2A or 2B, but 2T and 2R. Nice, neutral stuff that disguised nothing. When we gathered our bags and split into our intellectually cleansed classrooms, I remember a corrosive, colon-scouring sensation of shame. I can also remember the smell of the new room, dusty and ancient, with a faint tang of stale piss and mouse-shit. And envying the raucousness of those who clearly didn't give a rat's about the new demarcation. Their parents didn't care about T and R. Mine did.

Having a teacher for a parent is tricky anyway. They can smell bullshit the way a Springer scents a wounded bird. There's a remorseless inevitability about it, a refusal to entertain excuses, for the simple reason they've heard them all.

Having a father who'd emerged from a small 1940s North Kerry farm to earn a scholarship to a secondary school where everything, even Latin, was taught through Irish, and whose intelligence and self-assurance were so acute he spent the night before his Leaving Cert kick-off reading the *Sunday Press*, meant excuses as a currency were worse than useless.

I would have traded a decade of my life to avoid telling him. Months of dread revolved around his reaction. The walk home was crammed with painfully adolescent obsession, even worse than the months of anticipatory fears before that.

And it was bad. Even with hindsight, maybe half a decade would have been a fair swap. Diabolical predictions of a pass Inter Cert – this was a long time ago – and a failed Leaving Cert fought for oxygen with accusations of rank laziness in a seemingly never-ending tirade. My assurances, accurate as it happened, that the classes were being split for logistical purposes, and upper-level classes would be available to everyone, were dismissed as wishful thinking. My future was set – and it wasn't promising.

Except it wasn't set: it hadn't even started. How could it, at thirteen? The class assurances were true, as mostly were the accusations of laziness. And I ended up getting resolutely ordinary exam results, unexceptional, and very, very average.

I finished education in 1987, a dull, dark and consumptively awful time in almost every way. It makes the current economic and social climate look like Spring Break – whoo-hoo! Most youngsters hadn't an employment pot to pee in, at least not in Ireland. Aspiration wasn't a mouse-click away. The music was as lumpen as the fashion, both conspicuously lacking any sense of joy. And any possible sexual consolation required multiple layers of illegal latex products, as well as the production of a blood sample and a doctor's cert.

But, and this is the "but" I would stress to my thirteen-year-old self, it was the beginning: not the end of the beginning, not halfway, certainly not the end of anything. Once out of education's artificial cocoon, everything only started; a daunting idea in one way, but liberating too.

It doesn't mean you slide through school doing damn all. In fact, given the time again, it would be nice to relish the scholastic struggle more, attack the books with a bit of brio, always recognising though it is only a warm-up for the real deal.

That, though, is to indulge in the ultimate middle-aged fantasy: going back and applying what you know. Movies have been made about it. More males than will ever admit play similar personal movies through their brains long into adulthood. However, since that's the premise of this entire project, let's indulge a little, while realising such a fantasy is filmed through a prism that can never fully recapture the desperate self-consciousness of adolescence.

Someone very wise said if you don't look back five years and feel embarrassed at your younger self, then you're doing something wrong. In which case, yours truly, every day, and in every way, is getting better and better. Never mind five years: try one. And then guess at the crimson levels of embarrassment when it comes to over thirty.

Crippling self-consciousness at what your parents think of you is one thing; being even more preoccupied at what everyone else thinks of you is another. It took all my youth, and a tragically large part of afterwards, to stop spending ridiculously large amounts of time obsessed with what others might think of me.

A little bit of that is required to stop a person turning into a monster; too much testifies to obsession, and the ridiculous conceit that the world is as fascinated with you as you are.

So, note to thirteen-year-old self: relax. You might be tall, thin, built like a jockey's whip and in possession of a fresh, wispy "Ronnie" that really should feel a blade sometime soon, but you're not the only one like that. You might also find it daunting to initiate conversations with people you don't know, but that doesn't make you unique either. The idea of being the centre of attention is enough to make you want to puke, which contradicts an underlying suspicion that you know all the answers and need just a little encouragement to share them with everyone. But that contradiction isn't unheard of either.

Because here's the thing: anyone more interested in you than they are in themselves has bigger problems than coping with the yin-yang of insecurity and arrogance. And it's an unfortunate reality that in those rare cases when you're being considered at all, most people lean towards thinking the worst anyway, for the simple reason that they want to.

Anyway, enough theory, you say – gimme something practical, about stuff that really matters, like girls.

That's a toughie. Girls are different, simple as that. But not that different. Talk mightn't be your strong point but, if a girl actually speaks to you, that is not your cue to start desperately searching for a James Bond-type witty reply. Believe me, that is not your ace-in-the-hole.

So chat normally – or as normally as you can manage. Because here's the reality: when it comes to the sex-thing, or the kissy-thing, or the quick-fumble-at-the-back-of-the-sheds thing, it is always the girl who decides. There ain't a man alive whose slick patter has persuaded a woman to do something she doesn't want to – *ever*. And that includes you.

So, nothing fancy. Chat – if you can. But don't try too hard. Just remember the more you open your mouth, the more chance there is for putting your foot in it. Girls have a wonderful capacity for persuading themselves. You can only get in the way. Allow her to project all sorts of wonderfulness onto you.

A great way of helping that process along is a musical instrument: guitar is your safest bet. Tuba-players aren't famous for getting action. But chicks love guitars. And if you can play, and sing, then you will be a perfect blank screen for all kinds of projectors. So, start now, and persist, because you have no natural aptitude for music and waiting until adulthood will only mean failure. Believe me.

Now, when it comes to trying, actually do try a bit; and not just when it comes to the books. No one expects 100mph all the time but a gentle chugging fifty or sixty will do nicely. You'd be amazed what it might achieve. If nothing else, it will avoid the pitiful "if only" stuff that will beerily crop up years later.

You weren't too shabby a footballer at thirteen and beyond. And that was despite a horror of appearing to try at all. Throwing Jimmy Barry Murphy shapes was all very well but JBM managed to combine looking cool as hell on a field with actual effectiveness. Trying to be too-cool-for-school actually took far more energy than a bit of running around would have, and might have produced results that would have discouraged making for the sporting exit gates at the first available opportunity.

But that was all part of the self-consciousness thing. Like on the bus back from a schools match and everyone started singing that "We've got Johnny Smith, No. 1 . . . We've got the best team in the land" song: the sickening anxiety at the idea of the back of the bus getting to No. 10 and going "Who the hell is No. 10?" would have made you reach for the emergency cord if it had been a train. But they did know you. There wasn't much enthusiasm for their lazy-ass No. 10, but they did know you.

And if they hadn't, then so what? Embarrassment eventually goes away, honestly. It might not be fair that it comes back so readily, but that's another thing: forget fair, it doesn't exist. That isn't a cue to throw your hands up to heaven, just a reality it's best to square up to as quickly as possible. It's an unfair world but since it's the only one we've got, relish the struggle for what it is. And never resort to the most useless word in the language: *should*.

Instead face up to what is: and the most important "is" from that wringer of a day long ago came at the end. I was starting to doze off, when Dad knocked on the door, sat on the side of the bed and lightly squeezed my arm to end the pretence of sleep. All he said was, "Not to worry, Chief – we'll sort out something." Then he produced a packet of crisps and we shared them.

Because as a parent now myself, I know all that anger was only fear. Any idea your child might be vulnerable is appalling. He wasn't yelling at you – well, maybe a little – but really the yelling was a primal roar at a world that can be desperately tough even at the best of times. It was a roar from a gut knotted with the perpetual stress of worrying about your child. A different kind of worry, an admirable one, the sort of worry that makes you ready to fight the world if your kid is so much as looked at crooked. It's the worry I have for my kids now. It's also a reminder that someone else feels the same depth of love for me that I have for my own children.

You have to have kids of your own to fully get that. And when mine come to me at thirteen with similar news, I will absolutely go "tonto" too, forgetting everything and fearing everything. Because get this, Thirteen, worry never goes away.

You just get something more worthwhile to worry about, eventually, if you're lucky. And you are.

Brian O'Connor is the award-winning racing correspondent and sports columnist for the *Irish Times*. He has written three novels, *Bloodline*, *Threaten to Win* and *In the Picture* as well as a number of non-fiction books. Originally from County Cork, he now lives in County Wicklow. He is married to author Niamh O'Connor.

The Day Things Changed

Niamh O'Connor

It is 1979. I am Dorothy in *The Wizard of Oz* racing through the lanes of our estate on my chopper. A trick-or-treat bag of loot is hanging from the handlebars, and the Scarecrow – my brother Spud – is straddling the crossbar. Toto – Granny's Jack Russell – sticks his head out the top button of my coat, his bum secured by my coat's belt. We've covered Birches, Cherry Blossoms and Beeches, and have only the cul-de-sacs, Laurels and Fir Trees, to go before we dump the fruit, and head home with what's left: Sherbet, Cola Bottles, Flogs, and a packet of Rancheros.

Suddenly at the turn in the lane, I see our neighbour, Sinéad Roche, coming straight for us, a witch on boot-skates. I brake and stop.

Sinéad's got her mam's handbag over her shoulder like she has to go to the shops for bread or milk, only Sinéad never runs out of bread or milk, because she is an only child.

'Only children' collect fancy paper, which is paper with pictures on it, and is too good to write on, so Sinéad keeps hers in an empty biscuit tin, and I wish I was an only child with a whole box of biscuits in front of me that don't have to be stuffed in my mouth in case my brothers, AJ and Spud and Eskie, get them before me. I tried to save some fancy paper once that I scabbed off Sinéad with a horse's head on it, but Mam wrote *"washing-up liquid, soap, cooking oil, veg, sliced pan, mince and eggs"* over the eyes and ears.

Sinéad skids over to the handlebars and halts, using her stoppers, and "You have to go straight home," she says, and "Eskie's in an ambulance."

I know I will never be friends with her again, because of the way she says it, like her knowing before me is more important than just telling me what happened.

But I kind of guess what's wrong anyway, because yesterday me and Eskie were watching *"Spidahman, Spidahman, does whatever a spidah can"*, when the TV went all wonky and all you could see was fuzzy snow hopping all over the place. And Eskie kept staring at it and not getting bored, and his eyes didn't even blink, like he was asleep with his eyes open. I laughed, but Mam got scared.

When we get to Sinéad's house, her mother fries guggies for us and says, "Eskie had a turn. Does Spud eat eggs at home?" And I answer, "What, are you thick? Everyone knows he doesn't eat anything except crisps." No, I don't. I say, "Yes," just to see what will happen and she gives him a slap across the back of his head and tells him to "Eat up," and he lays his shoe right into my shin under the table, the shitehawk. I have to bite my own tongue to stop telling Sinéad's mam the white of her eggs looks like snots and Mam never hits us.

I didn't ask her what a turn was, but when Eskie came home from hospital I saw one. I heard Mam upstairs kind of screaming for Dad to come, and he goes belting down the stairs, and Eskie is lying on the floor shaking like mad, and his eyes are going mental and his lip is pumping blood from where he banged it off the door when the turn took him, and Dad comes back up the stairs with the spoon for eating boiled eggs with St Patrick on it. Mam shouts to get her rosary beads off the locker, and Dad shoves me out of the way when I give them to her, even though

I'm trying to see how much of St Patrick's hat is sticking out of Eskie's mouth to stop him swallowing his tongue.

I must have a short tongue because there's no way I can swallow mine, and I try all the time in bed even when I think I'm not trying, because it's my new habit. My old one was bending my fingers back to see if I'm double-jointed.

When I get back out of bed to ask Dad to tuck me in so Jack Frost can't get me, he says, "Get into the car" and "There's nobody here to mind you" and "No, there isn't time to go to Granny's first," or even to put my tracker on. Nobody hears me in the car when I say, "I can't move my legs" in my Bionic Woman in-the-first-episode voice because my skin's stuck to the car seats in my nightie. The pain makes a game of "Help, my legs are paralysed" though. After that, I have a game of stick my finger out the window because I have turned invisible. If you stick your head out Dad kills you, but he doesn't know about my little finger, ha ha. Like the only way not to die of boredom when you're in the yard before roll call is to squeeze your bum in and out. If you talk, or move, *múinteoir* gives you lines, but he can't see who's squeezing their bums at him. All of our class have dimpley bums from doing it after Nigel Doherty invented it. You nearly break your shite laughing if you see somebody else doing it before you think of it.

AJ doesn't give out that he has to sit in the middle, with me and Spud at the window seats, because he wants to show off to Dad he knows the way to the hospital from getting his verruca cut off, and he leans between Mam and Dad and Eskie's leg pointing in the air the same direction as St Patrick still stuck in his mouth.

When that game is over I play the toy ads so I don't have to listen to Mam crying. You know when Christmas is coming because all the toy ads are on the telly. The best ones are the Incredible Hulk doll because you can turn him inside out and he's not David Banner any more. Spud wants Buckaroo. You put all the things on the donkey's back and he kicks them off and you lose. AJ wants a BMX bike because they are the best for wheelies. Eskie wants everything he sees. I want a magic kit. Mam always says we will get a surprise. Dear God, it will only be a surprise if it's a magic kit.

AJ made me want it. He wrapped cling film around his finger and made a hole in a box of Cara to put his blue finger in. Then he opened the box and wiggled. "Abracadabra, hey presto, Geronimo, ladies and gentlemen, I give you a finger without a hand!" "Jesus," Mam said the first time and her shoulders jumped. Dad killed him for emptying the matches and I think he put a cricket behind our fridge to hum every time we opened it to rob cling film. But it was worth getting into trouble. Like the time AJ invented a competition to see who could pick the biggest lump of rust off Dad's Fiat 127 without it breaking. It could have been a photo finish with the bit I was getting over the tyre except Eskie ran inside and asked Dad did he want to play. Now AJ holds the world championship for getting a piece as big as his little finger off the boot and there's no chance of a rematch.

Eskie ruins everything. His real name is Muirtey which is short for Martin, but the fur on his anorak hood makes him look like an Eskimo, Spud said, and it stuck, even though Mam goes mental if she hears us calling him that. Some nights when he thinks Jabbah the Hutt is under the bottom bunk, Mam lets him up the ladder in with me. If he puts his toe-jammy freezing feet near me I go "Eskie, Eskie, Eskie" a million times and he cries because he hates that name, and Mam has to take him in with her. Except for the time he stood on a rusty nail and was allowed to do anything he wanted like one of the Billy Barry kids on the *Late Late Toy Show*. He got my bunk to himself even after I offered to suck out the poison for a trade, but he wouldn't let me and what did he do then only wet my bed, and Mam had to put a bin bag under him, and the noise drove me mental all night every time he moved, and I couldn't even kick my own mattress from underneath.

And another reason I hate him is for always hanging around before I go up the hill in our estate for my Mount Everest game. Sometimes I have to climb that mountain without any brandy if there is an avalanche because of him. Every day, Dad drives down it after work at half five. So I climb Mount Everest to wait for him. When Dad sees me he pulls in and turns off the engine and lets me steer the car down the hill. Mam keeps telling him to be careful, but he says I help him save petrol. I love Dad. If Eskie ever tries to have a go at driving down the hill again I'll burst him, because of all the petrol he is wasting making us go to the hospital.

I never wanted to go to bed before, but I do in the car park of the hospital. I could put the pillow over my head and Mam wouldn't be making that noise. She would be singing, "Dona, Dona, Dona, Dona" about the calf on a wagon bound for market and the swallow flying freely in the sky above him and the winds laughing with all their might. We all have our own lullaby. Mam would never sing yours to someone else. They can listen in their room but it's not for them. The same as when she was pregnant she ate different things for all of us: tongue for AJ, coal and firelighters for Spud, Brussels sprouts for me, and Turkish Delights for Eskie.

Even though we are here now, Mam keeps crying, and would she ever stop, but she won't, and she won't give Eskie to Dad or the doctors and nurses either. Eskie is as blue as AJ's magic finger, but Mam is blaming the tinfoil, not the cling film. "He got too hot when I made him be the Tin Man," she says. She wrapped his arms and legs in tin foil, and me and Spud kept picking the bits of chewing-gum cheese left over from Dad's lunches out of it, before we went off on the chopper to do the roads.

"Dona, dona, dona, dona," is the bit where the moo-cow is crying for its mam. Baby birds shoved out by an orphan cuckoo cry too on the way down. Tadpoles are the shape of tears, but nobody can tell me if they cried in the Hoover. I took them home for the summer holidays, but Eskie kept looking at them, and I don't know if he did it on purpose, but he knocked the bowl over. First he pretended he didn't know, but "Confess, confess, confess," said Spud and got him in a headlock and he did. Their legs were supposed to grow in our house and not in the Hoover which Dad wouldn't empty because Mam hadn't lost any jewellery. I forgot to claim Eskie for it, and now I'm never going to get a chance because he's probably dead.

Ourfatherwhoartinheavenhallowedbethynamethykingdomco methywillbedoneonearthasitisinheavengiveusthisdayourdailybre adandforgiveusourtresspassesasweforgivethosewhotrespassagai nstusandleadusnotintotemptationbutdeliverusfromevilifSantagiv esmeamagickitIwilldoanythingyouwantamen.

Niamh O'Connor is the true-crime editor of the *Sunday World* newspaper and the author of the true-crime books *The Black Widow*, *Cracking Crime* and *Blood Ties*. She has written four novels in the Jo Birmingham series: *If I Never See You Again*, *Taken*, *Too Close For Comfort* and *Blink*. She is married to author and *Irish Times* racing correspondent, Brian O'Connor, and they have three children.

The Frog Prince

Fintan O'Higgins

My life was blighted by my erotic fixation on a seven-year-old girl.

I was seven too, and although I had never heard the word "erotic" I knew one thing: I wanted, above everything else in life, to kiss this child. Alison was pretty and blonde and smiled a lot. I think even at the time I knew there was no really deep spiritual bond between us, but I wanted there to be. I wanted to smell her hair and hold her hand. I wanted her physically, and even if I didn't know what I would do with her physically if I had her, I *did* know that it involved kissing. Kissing, getting married and living happily ever after were things which seemed inextricable to me as a seven-year-old and such was the overpowering strength of my feelings for Alison, they seemed also to be destined by Fate. That she and I would kiss, marry and live happily ever after was one of those happy inevitabilities. It was exciting to have a destiny, to have the progress of my life and love written in the stars. I was quite sure that this destiny would be fulfilled because it was inconceivable to me that it should not, the Universe being fair-minded and benign.

The certainty of our fairytale ending did not, however, bring with it peace of mind. I walked through those days when I was in First Class in a state of dizzy agitation. A giddy excitement stirred up my whole body. I was dazed by love; I was overwhelmed with it; I was drowning in the stuff. Days were measured by time spent with her; I gauged distance by how far away she was. I made excuses to talk to her, deliberately breaking the nib of my pencil so I could borrow her pink see-through sharpener with the sparkles and hearts. I hung my coat on the hook beside hers and lingered while she hung up her jacket so I could brush her grey-jumpered elbow with my own and catch, briefly and maddeningly, the scent of her blonde hair. We sometimes played together in the yard, apart from the others, and more than once during these games she caught me looking at her, waiting for her to smile in recognition of our shared love and destiny. She never did, though, and I had to admit to being disappointed by her failure to acknowledge our mutual passion, which I assumed was too enormous and important to require words to communicate itself.

I made the mistake of telling my mother about my intention to make Alison my bride. She thought this was adorable. Since my feelings for Alison were profound, mysterious and disturbing, I considered my mother's amusement very crass. And when she told her friends about my little romance and they laughed about it, charmed, I was humiliated and resolved never to tell my mother anything important ever again (I still don't). In any case, it made sense to keep my love a private matter. In a class full of seven-year-old boys with less rarefied romantic sensibilities than my own, this soppiness towards a girl was not the sort of thing you wanted to advertise. (I had never found girls yucky, although I pretended to, and when years later the other boys in my class admitted to liking them I felt an odd mixture of relief, unwelcome competition and that certain smug pride: "Girls? Yeah, I've been into them since way back, when they were just starting out . . .")

So I walked around with my secret. I was intoxicated by the love that swilled around my belly like some dark, sweet poison.

It made me feel special and different, but isolated. I needed to share my secret and Alison, for all her refusal to communicate with me telepathically during our games, seemed the natural person to talk to. I asked her to marry me, and she consented. Gavin Cleary officiated at the wedding which took place in the school yard one lunch time. I had grave misgivings about telling him my plans – he was a gossip and he played with the girls – but he claimed to know the words to the ceremony so I had no choice. When the time came, it irked me that he was clearly making it up as he went along. It compromised the seriousness of the occasion. We got to the part where I was supposed to kiss Alison. It should have been a moment of perfect happiness for me. I was just turning to my new bride, about to look her solemnly in the eye and pucker up, when Gavin began giggling. I glared at him. He giggled more then he shouted out in his giddy-whiny voice, calling people over to see us kissing. In a moment a small group was gathering to gawk at Alison and me, and a chorus of "Kissin'! *Kis*-sin'! Kis-*siiinnnnnn*'!" went up, desecrating the holy moment. Alison ran off embarrassed. I was left red-faced and furious to face the pack of baying children, the girls thrilled, the boys disgusted by the sight. I struggled to squeeze back a tear. I wanted to punch Gavin Cleary right on the nose. I wish I had.

After the disaster of the wedding our games together became less frequent, but my love for Alison was as overwhelming as ever, and was now causing me some distress. Still, I knew that she and I were destined to be together, and it became apparent that the agents of Destiny were to be Mr and Mrs Nicholl.

My later dealings with resting actors who take gigs teaching drama in primary schools have made me question my judgement of the time, but back then Mr and Mrs Nicholl impressed me as the most glamorous and inspiring couple in the scintillating history of show-business. They wore colourful jumpers and baggy dungarees. Their gestures were expansive and their voices went up and down a lot. They wore hats, both of them, indoors.

Mr and Mrs Nicholl taught us the essential components of

the actor's craft: how to sway like the wind, how to be a tree. It was a rigorous training in the classic tradition and it prepared us for our big class project, which was to put on a show, *The Frog Prince*. The text was probably chosen because of its classic fairytale elements: a princess, a transmogrification, a marriage and gold. For me, though, it will always be the story of a frog trying to become a prince, and it reminds me of how if I had had the courage to ennoble myself to that royal estate, my life would have been quite different. I am not Prince Charming, nor was meant to be, as the poet said.

Alison's personal beauty made her the obvious choice to play the princess. Conor Dolan was cast as the prince. He had the profile of a handsome grown-up and a pretty regal bearing for a seven-year-old. Conor was a friend of mine but the thought of him marrying my princess was hard to take. When he approached me and expressed the shy hope that I would not think him soppy because he had to marry the Princess and, worse, *kiss* her, I stared at him in outrage and pity and ferocious jealousy and kept my secret to myself.

I started rehearsals as a dream-sprite but found myself rising through the ranks of daffodils and fairies to more substantial roles. I was soon elevated to the position of a page, and thence – owing to my prodigious talent for knowing where I was supposed to stand and Conor Dolan's inability to remember his lines – to the title role. I suppose the Nicholls' reasoning was that since they couldn't get a decent prince to play the part they might as well make use of a fairly serviceable frog, which I was.

I liked being a frog and I was pretty good at it. Frogs seemed to me superior to princes in most respects. Talking frogs are funny, talking princes are not; frogs have cool slippery skin and hilarious googly eyes and can hold their breaths for ages at a time; princes just hang around with sceptres and things, which is fine if that is what you are into, but on the whole given the choice between being a frog and being a prince, I found my natural tastes and talents lay consistently with the ranine.

The one thing a prince has going for him, however, is that he gets to kiss princesses. You don't get to kiss princesses unless you man up and assume the dignity and bearing of a prince, unless you do something brave or difficult to earn her.

It was very exciting to play the Frog Prince. A neighbour, Helen Byrne, made me a green felt frog mask. It had eyes made of a split ping-pong ball and a pink velvet lining and it made me look very like Kermit the Frog. (It even had a Kermitty uvula and Kermit's uvula is perhaps the most famous in the business.) To this day I feel a great deal of kinship with the put-upon Muppet frog.

I also had a red satin cloak. The cloak was made by the same neighbour (a friend of our teacher Mrs Kelly, it turned out, and I remember the shock of understanding for the first time that it was possible for a teacher to exist outside the classroom) and it was beautifully put together with red lining and a special princely-looking clasp at the throat. This cape was to be kept for the critical moment in the drama when my character was transformed. I had to duck behind a covered table, remove my Kermit head, put on the red satin cloak (and a crown) and assume my princely form. Helen Byrne and my mother both thought that I looked very handsome as a little prince, but although I liked the cloak and considered it very good for being a vampire, I was not really that interested in being a prince, and when the crucial moment came I discovered that I was not prince material anyway.

Of course it was an honour to be cast in the title role of this exciting and challenging piece, but the really thrilling part was that I got to marry Alison, and kiss her. I could not think about anything else. I felt as if I was being inflated like some happy balloon and might drift skyward at any minute. I watched kissing couples on television and in the street and felt very privileged and important that I was soon to join their ranks. When we rehearsed I was a professional – on time, off book, committed – and I never forgot that we were not yet married, that this was just a rehearsal. When we went over the early scenes where the princess rejects the frog I knew, although I could not control the awful feeling of rejection in the immediate moment, that true love was going to triumph and that Alison and I were going to end the play standing together on stage, hand in hand and married.

And all the time I dreamed of kissing her. The thought of pushing aside her blonde hair and touching her cheek with my lips made me more happy and giddy than I had ever been before. Waiting for my mother to pick me up after rehearsals one afternoon, I sat looking out at the dark rainy day and caught my reflection. Without really thinking about it I pursed my lips. It looked stupid, but I persisted. I watched my face as it drew near to the ghostly image in the glass. The hard persistent rattle of the rain on the window sent a shiver up my spine in the stuffy classroom. My lips approached those of my reflection and I leaned forward on my elbows, over the grey mottled plastic of the school table, and I kissed the pane like a sad, silly little Narcissus. The glass was cold and flat and I immediately pulled away, feeling very stupid but thrilling still to the thought that soon I would be kissing a real face, Alison's. As I withdrew my mouth from the window, I saw Mrs Nicholl behind me, reflected in the glass. I turned around in a sweaty panic of embarrassment. She told me quietly that my mother had arrived to collect me, but she had a look of grown-up concern on her face that made me sick with worry.

At our next rehearsal Mr and Mrs Nicholl announced that because we were *all* part of the show and because it was *fun* to decide things together as an artistic collective, we were going to take a vote on the ending of the play. There were two endings to choose from.

The first ending was the traditional one: because the princess has allowed the frog to sleep on her pillow he is transformed into a handsome prince. She is persuaded, as so many women have been, that he really has changed for the better, accepts his suit, and marries him. In this version Alison and I were to hold hands, kiss, take our bow and leave the stage to live happily ever after together. This is the proper ending, the correct ending, the ending that all nature cries out for.

The other ending was described, in a phrase that took on a very bitter irony for me, as "the funny ending". In this perversion of the natural order of things, the prince – having undertaken to find the princess's golden ball at the bottom of the pond, having elicited from the princess an undertaking that he may eat from her plate and sleep on her pillow as his reward, having written her a little song and having, by any reasonable standards, wooed the living bejaysus out of her – rejects the woman he has struggled so hard to win, saying something utterly fatuous like "Oh no, Princess, I could never marry a woman who sleeps with frogs!"

As if a proper lover would act like that, as if any prince worthy of the name would be so stupid as to destroy his own happiness for the sake of a lame joke like that! The spiteful twist at the end of the "funny" version seemed designed to give my princess her comeuppance. It is true that the girl in the story is a little bratty. She is openly rude to the frog, makes some quite cruel remarks about his physical appearance and would renege on her deal with him if her father did not insist that she keep her word. But she's a princess, so what do you expect? We could have made it work.

We raised our hands one by one to vote, first the girls and then the boys. There were more boys than girls in the class and I wonder now if Mrs Nicholl was counting on the votes being divided along lines of sex. The girls, with admirable artistic discernment, voted unanimously for the ending with the kissy stuff, and my heart leaped in my breast when I saw Alison's hand go up, an earnest of our plighted troth.

Then it was the boys' turn. We voted on the funny ending first and about fourteen hands went up. I kept my hand down. It wasn't "about" fourteen hands; it was exactly fourteen. There were twenty-nine in our class, fourteen girls and fifteen boys. Fourteen boys had voted for the funny ending. Fourteen girls had voted for the real ending, the true ending.

"Now," Mrs Nicholl said, and she was looking at me as she said it. "The romantic ending – hands up?"

I could have put my hand up. I could have had my happy ending. I could have kissed Alison and become a prince. But I remembered the jeers that had spoiled the solemnity of the wedding, my mother's kindly but humiliating laughter, the impossibility of explaining to the world feelings which I was too small to understand myself. Mrs Nicholl looked at me, I looked away. I shook my head with a tiny movement, barely turning my neck at all as I stared at my blue shoes, my chin almost on my jumper and a shameful red heat moving up my spine to my cheeks. I had been offered an opportunity to raise my hand, to determine my future, to claim my woman and to act like a prince, but I bottled out and, in bottling out, condemned myself to the funny ending.

The play went on and I was accounted a pretty successful Frog Prince. I looked to Alison for some hint of regret but carried on acting when it did not come. I even got a laugh. A laugh is not a kiss. And, as I played that last idiotic line – "I could never marry a woman who sleeps with frogs!" – and smiled with professional modesty as the crowd of parents laughed and clapped, I was a bit like Shaw watching the applause that greeted *Arms and the Man*: the only person in the theatre who knew that the whole affair was a ghastly failure. But for me it was a personal failure rather than an artistic one.

For the rest of my time in primary school I continued to hanker after Alison. Everybody knew it though I never had the courage to admit it. Even now I am not sure if Mrs Nicholl engineered the whole changed ending out of some prurient disapproval of my seven-year-old's longing. It doesn't matter: she tested my love and my love was found wanting. And even though for years after, those long years of eight and nine and ten years old, although I still cherished the hope that Alison and I would get to live happily ever after, I also knew that I had blown my chances that day, when I failed to become a prince and condemned myself to being a frog forever.

Fintan O'Higgins is a writer from Dublin. His professional work has included storylines and scripts for television soap operas *Emmerdale*, *Fair City* and *Ros na Rún*, as well as a feature film, *Capsizing the Stars* (Blueprint Pictures, supported by the IFB) and stage plays, including *The Departure Lounge*, commissioned by Rough Magic as part of their Seeds programme. His poetry, fiction, essays, translations and criticism have appeared in *The Stinging Fly*, *Comhar*, *The Raintown Review*, the *University of Alabama's Birmingham Poetry Review* and elsewhere. He has performed his poetry around the country, at the international Literary Death Match, the Brownbread Mixtape, and Nighthawks, both in Dublin and as part of the Electric Picnic. He has won various small prizes.

Irn-Bru and Déjà Vu

Geraldine O'Neill

The difficult thing about imagining if you were a child again is that you always think you would go back and relive your life more brilliantly with the adult brain and experience you have now. How fantastic that would be! Or would it?

You might drive yourself – or everyone else – mad because you would be out of step with all the other kids your own age, looking at things the way grown-ups do. Children usually take each minute, each day and each event as it comes, while older people tend to plan and analyse things.

And what if you were only going back in time for one single day? Wouldn't it be a better idea to enjoy every minute doing all the things you loved when you were a child?

Thinking about this brought back memories of routines and episodes in my younger life that I hadn't recalled in decades. Different things came flooding back into my mind about growing up in Cleland, a small mining village in Scotland, in our lively family home with four sisters and a younger brother. Apart from my parents, we also had our Papa (Dad's elderly uncle) living with us – a quiet gentle Irishman who we all loved. Our local school was only a minute's walk away – so close that we could see the schoolyard out of the windows at the back of the house.

If I could go back in time, here are some of the things I would choose to do again:

I would love to relive a Christmas Day when I was about nine years old. I think this is a good age, as I still had Santa to look forward to, and with so many children, our house would be full of excitement and discussion about him coming for months before. It was usually very cold in Scotland at that time of year, and if we didn't have snow to look forward to, there was often frost and ice, which were almost as exciting. From October onwards we would be playing out in the street in our knitted pixie hats and gloves, making slides, and if we were lucky building snowmen in the gardens.

The night before Christmas we would all be bathed and have our hair washed and we would sit around the big coal fire in our pyjamas and dressing-gowns eating fruit. We usually had small bowls with half of an enormous orange or an apple my mother had carefully peeled and quartered for us. Occasionally we had something different like a pomegranate, which took ages eating with a teaspoon.

My mother bought the fruit from a local man who drove around the villages in a converted single-decker bus three evenings a week. I can still picture the green-painted bus, with the owner – Matt Robertson – dressed in his brown shop-assistant's overall, standing behind the long wooden counters. I can easily recall the citrusy smell of the boxes of fruit he had on the shelves (which had a lip on them to stop them sliding off when he turned the corners) and the open sacks of potatoes, carrots and onions.

Matt also sold things like tins of peas and packets of dried lentils, and I always think of him when I see a small tin of my mother's favourite white butter beans.

While we were eating our fruit we usually watched television – shows like *The London Palladium* or *Steptoe and Son*, or, if it was a Saturday night, we would sit glued to a wrestling match, cheering on the popular wrestlers like Mick MacManus, Kendo Nagasaki or Jackie Pallo.

Around nine o'clock, we would all be shooed to bed where we would lie for hours whispering about the toys and sweets we hoped to get the following morning.

It was during those nights when the only light in the room came from the yellow streetlamp outside our window that my two younger sisters, Kathleen and Patricia (who shared the room with me) would ask me to tell them a story and my imagination would run riot. I could make a story up in minutes, adding yards to it as I went along. We all had a comic each delivered to the house on various days – *Bunty*, *Judy*, *The Dandy* and *The Beano*. Often, Kathleen or Patricia would ask me to make up the next episode of The Four Marys or one of the other serial stories. Of course my version was usually more dramatic than the way the comic told it, and although they often giggled to each other at my unbelievable, far-fetched versions, they never really complained. It was either listen to me or lie bored in the dark.

On Christmas morning, we would race to the sitting-room, where Santa always left our toys and books in specific corners. He would have thoughtfully written our names on a piece of card on top of each individual pile, to avoid any mix-ups or arguments.

The toys I would love to go back and play with would be the tiny tinkling piano, the kaleidoscope which kept me quietly entertained for hours, and the Etch-A-Sketch and the fantastic books which came from my mother's pen-friend in America. Books featured largely, and we always had three or four each, including annuals like *Oor Wullie*, *The Broons*, *The Dandy* and *Beano*. And one of the biggest treats – a whole Cadbury's Selection Box each.

After we had played with the toys for a while, my mother would make us sit down and eat lovely fresh morning rolls filled with boiled or scrambled eggs. Then, we would get dressed in our best clothes for ten o'clock Mass, where we would meet all our friends and neighbours and have a great chat about the presents we had got.

We had an early dinner of goose (which came from our grandfather in Ireland) with potato stuffing and roast potatoes, followed by home-made trifle. Afterwards, the children would be deposited in the biggest bedroom where we would sit in front of the fire eating our Selection Boxes and reading the American books like *The Bobbsey Twins* and *Little Women*.

The rest of Christmas Day slipped by as we watched films on television and played our new games of Bingo or Snakes and Ladders with Mum, Dad and Papa. Later we would all sit and listen to my elder sister Teresa's new pop records on the radiogram, eat more chocolate and read. Very few friends called to the house that day, as it was tradition to spend it with the family.

Reviewing my choice of day to relive as a child, I can think of a few other days I might well have picked – Easter Sunday, with all the same excitement over the Easter eggs, and wearing our new dresses and straw hats to Mass. Then, later, if the weather was fine, going on a picnic to the "Big Hill" to roll our hard-boiled eggs down it and then eat them along with sandwiches and Irn-Bru.

I would also love to go back and spend an ordinary day around the house, spending time with my parents, Papa, and my sisters and little brother. School was fine, but not fine enough for me to relive for one precious day, so I would probably pick a Saturday when I was around twelve years old. I would get up early, before my parents and siblings, and sit with Papa drinking a cup of hot milk and a slice of toasted Mother's Pride plain bread.

Although I loved all the chatter and banter of a big family, occasionally I loved those quiet mornings with just me and Papa. Later, I would go up to the library to change my clutch of books and chat to the librarian and any friends who were there. It was always interesting as you never knew who you might meet. I would then come home and have something like a Scottish pie or a Bridie, and then I would set off out again, over to my neighbours who I ran errands for every Saturday. I first would go to Rose, who was an invalid, living with her husband, Joe Alenskas, her adopted son Joseph and her brother James. I loved going to their house because Rose treated me more as an adult than anyone else did, plus she was very funny and used bad language, which my parents never did.

I would head up to the local Co-Operative store with my list of shopping, calling for my friend, Ella, on the way. We would dawdle around the shops for an hour or two then meander back. Then, clutching my half a crown from Rose, I would make my way further up the street to Mrs Collins, and after chatting over some of her home-made cakes and a glass of her dandelion (non-alcoholic) wine, I would go for her shopping which would earn me another half a crown. In the evening we would have dinner around the kitchen table and afterwards I would go down to a friend's house to sit in her bedroom listening to records.

When I look back at my choice of days to relive, I can see it was all about enjoying my family, neighbours and friends – and talking, eating and reading. Not a lot different from today except I might be chatting over a glass of wine as opposed to an Irn-Bru!

Looking back generally, I have countless pieces of advice I'd give my younger self.

Love and cherish all the people who are good to you. Let them know how much you think of them. They won't always be there and as you get older you will realise that love is the most important thing in life.

Try to find your own path in life, the things you love doing etc., as it will make you a happier and more fulfilled person. Whilst being as kind and thoughtful to other people as you can, don't put yourself last. It's very important to live your life for yourself and not feel resentful that you spent most of your time pleasing others.

Be grateful for the good things in life. Always thank people who have been kind to you or given you gifts or shared their precious time with you. When we do something nice for someone and are met with ingratitude, it puts us off doing it again. Ingratitude is something people might notice and remember about you.

Talk and explain why you are doing things in a certain way, how you feel about situations, whether you like something or not etc. Other people can't read our minds, and if we aren't clear then wrong assumptions can easily be made.

Friends come in all shapes and sizes. Don't judge or dismiss other people because they are different to you – and be as kind as you can to everyone. Don't judge people on their looks, their race, religion, class or their ability at things. When I was younger I had several much older friends who I learned from. Now, when I have grown-up children, I have friends who are much younger than me – and I still learn from them!

Notice all the beauty around you that nature and other people give us – flowers, artwork, beautiful scenery, music. Just looking at beautiful things does our heart and our mind good and relaxes us.

Life is exciting – live every day as fully as you can. Get all the things you *have to do* (like homework and any chores) over with so you can spend the rest of the time doing things you love.

Look after your health as you want your body to stay in good nick as long as possible. Definitely do not smoke! Apart from the horrible smells that will hang around you, it gives you lines and wrinkles – and smoking *kills people*. My beautiful younger sister was a heavy smoker from her teens and died much too soon – leaving three small children – because of it. Be wary of alcohol and drugs too – they can alter your brain forever and make you do things on the spur of the moment that can have huge consequences.

Walk as much as you can and notice the great feeling it gives you. Notice what's going on around you whether it's in the town or the country. Try out as many physical things you can, like swimming, running, badminton etc., until you find something you love. Competitive sports aren't for everyone and there are lots of other things out there.

If you read constantly you will never be bored and you will always be learning. It fills all the boring little gaps in your life while you're waiting – books, magazines, online features. Join a library – apart from the books, you can borrow DVDs and CDs and you can even read magazines for free! It's also a fantastic place to find out what's going on in all the nearby towns. Books are friends for life! I can still remember all the brilliant books I read as a child and I learned from every one of them.

Experiment with subjects in school and with hobbies until you find something you love. It can be anything from learning to play the guitar, knitting, chess, drawing, writing stories. There are loads of things out there so there's got to be something you will enjoy – and you will meet new friends who like the same things as you.

When something serious is worrying you, talk to your parents or a close relative or a nice teacher about it. Try to remember that things change quickly and a week later the problem might all be forgotten. If you have to work things out or make an important decision – give yourself a break from it by doing something nice and then, when you are more relaxed, the answer will often come to you.

If you want to do something or have something, and feel it is out of your reach – imagine having it already. It really works! (Not completely *always* – but often.) It's called visualisation and people like famous athletes have used it to imagine themselves winning races.

If you've made a mistake, done something stupid or hurt someone – apologise! Your body often lets you know if you're in the wrong because it will niggle away at you, making you run the incident over and over in your mind, and sometimes it gives you a sinking feeling in your stomach. We all make mistakes and if you are in the wrong an apology will sort it out 99% of the time.

Learn how to manage money as early on as you can. I was rubbish at it and spent every penny I earned from my teenage Saturday jobs on buying clothes and going to discos. If I had to go back in time now, I would save one tenth of everything I had so that I always had something put away if something big like an unexpected holiday came up. Extra money also lets you buy gifts and treat other people, and the feeling you get from being generous is bigger than receiving gifts!

While spending time with family and friends is really important, discover the joy of spending time on your own. Apart from reading and your hobbies, take time to just sit thinking about nothing in particular. It's relaxing and good for you.

Lastly, be kind to yourself.

Geraldine O'Neill has published ten novels and written numerous short stories and features for newspapers and magazines. Her books are set in the almost-forgotten Ireland of the 1950s and 1960s. Her writing covers many themes, but the common thread that runs through her work is that of emigration. She grew up in Cleland, Lanarkshire, in Scotland and has lived with her family in County Offaly since 1991. She trained as a school teacher and has enjoyed many years teaching in Scotland, England and latterly, at her local school in Daingean. You can find out more about Geraldine at www.geraldine-oneill.com.

Light Within the Dark

Louise Phillips

A number of years back a woman I had briefly met asked me a straightforward question. "What kind of a childhood did you have?" My answer was both short and swift. "Don't go there," I said. Thankfully she took the hint, and didn't. But I still remember the emotional torrent behind my response, even if the woman in question wasn't aware of it. Internally, a tsunami of emotional defence-mechanisms jumped into place. The truth was: *I couldn't go there.*

Yes, like many, I'd often reflected on my childhood. But to share, to open up, or to discuss any of it, other than with those closest to me, felt as if the large gaping hole lying beneath might still be capable of swallowing me up like quicksand.

I look on writing this piece as an opportunity, not just for me, but for anyone, young or old, who has looked back and seen, felt, or experienced, things they wished they hadn't.

If I was a child again, I would tell my younger self that there is always light within the dark. I would also tell her not to be so scared. I would ask her to trust me when I say the world around us is made up of all kinds of people and things – some of them can make you feel afraid, some of them can make you feel sadness, but even those who wittingly or unwittingly cause you pain often have a bigger picture that as a child it is impossible to recognise or understand. Children are like sponges, they soak up everything, but there is one component that is more important than anything else: the knowledge that someone cares. If I was a child again, I would whisper to my younger self, "Even those who cause you sadness can love you deeply."

We grew up in poverty. Many others did too, so nothing unusual there. The difference comes in part from the *where*, and in part from the *how*. I was born in Mount Pleasant Buildings, one of the worst squalor-holes of Dublin city. There were fewer than three years between my brother Tom, my sister Phil, and me. We were born likes steps of stairs, one after the other, and I was the youngest. My mother became pregnant twice after me: the first baby, a girl, died of cot death when she was five days old; the second and final pregnancy was a boy. He was stillborn at seven months. My mother referred to both of them as her angels in heaven. Looking back, poverty and poor nourishment must have played their part. But it wasn't poverty or poor nourishment which overshadowed my childhood; it was the overprotection of my mother, and the anger of my father.

My mother didn't want us to mix with other children from the tenements. She looked on our accommodation in an aspirational sense, as "temporary", but one that lasted until I was eleven years old. Undoubtedly, she was ashamed of where we lived, and this shame lodged firmly in all our psyches. She didn't want others, including those at the school we attended, to know where we lived, so she concocted a false address. We actually lived at 25 Mount Pleasant Building, but the flat was on the outer edges of the tenements, forming part of Oxford Road, so to everyone outside of our family, including those at school, we lived at 25 Oxford Road.

It's not an easy thing to live a lie as a four-year-old. In fact, even now, lying makes me feel extremely uncomfortable. I'm the world's worst poker player. I hate lying, which is possibly why writing fiction feels like a good thing to do. Making things up when they are make-believe is okay, but lying isn't.

One difficulty was that I couldn't bring friends home from school, and I couldn't befriend those at home either. It meant at times living a kind of secret-agent existence – one world not knowing about the other. On school mornings, I would stand on the front steps, looking up and down Oxford Road. If I saw someone I knew from school, I would stay in the shadows and, as soon as the coast was clear, I would dart up the street in an effort to get past the tenements before anyone had seen where I had come from.

It's hard to write these things because knowing that as a child I had an inbuilt sense of shame about where I lived, which led ultimately to creating an inbuilt sense of shame about myself, is difficult. Our outdoor play restrictions meant that, for a large part of my childhood, I was cocooned within the world of a tiny flat. The main respite was school, which I loved, and trips to the library with my mother, or the odd visit to the pictures with my father – funny that both of these external environments were extensions of a fictional life.

For the most part, I'm a confident person, one who communicates with ease, but those early days have left their scars. I recognise that I missed out on developing elements of social interaction that others experienced. I also recognise that even as an adult there are times I can still feel as vulnerable as that young schoolgirl hiding in the shadows, the one who was ashamed for no good reason. If I was a child again, I would rewind that tape. I would tell my younger self that she should be proud, that her feelings of not being as good as everyone else were false, superimposed by a shame she was too young to quantify or understand. I would tell her she did great, and there is always light within the dark.

The light for me was that I came to love books; those trips to the library opened up my world. When I went to the cinema, the heroes and heroines on the big screen were larger than life – they fascinated me. I dreamt of one day becoming a writer. I also dreamt of being a singer, even though I hadn't a note in my head!

My imaginary world became my best friend, because I needed one.

As an adult, I can reflect on aspects of my mother's life that I couldn't understand as a child. I can see clues in photographs. There was a time when my mother used to make our clothes. There are black-and-white photos of myself and my sister in pretty dresses, ones that my mother had sewn. Then things changed. We started getting our clothes from second-hand shops, and we smelt on account of the fact that we were rarely washed. We had lice in our hair, wore shoes belonging to someone else. This wasn't just because we were poor. I know that now. Having gone through post-natal depression on each of my three pregnancies, I now partly understand what my mother must have gone through after losing both her babies. Back then there was no help for women who lived my mother's life. She would have been told to get on with things. She sank for a long time. I know that too, even if as a child I couldn't understand it. I have utterly no doubt that she loved us, and if I could go back I would hug her for no good reason – I would hug her every minute of every day, because it was hard for her too.

My father was an angry man. If I was a child again, I would tell my younger self that none of his anger was because of me. Like my mother, his world was harsh. There was little work, and many mouths to feed. In my lifetime, I got to know two fathers, both of them the same man. I got to know the father who pushed his grandchildren in their buggies, who played with them, and loved them with all his heart. As a child I had known the aggressive man, the one who would take his anger out on us, and who made my mother's life a living hell. To everyone else he was someone who cracked silly jokes, who opened the front door with a smile. But once that door was closed, he changed. I know alcohol played its part too. It always darkened his mood.

I recall thinking how much better our life would be if he were dead. I have a memory of looking at him in the back bedroom of the flat that myself and my sister shared with our parents, and thinking how much happier we would all be if he was gone. As

I contemplated this, I worked out that we would have no financial support without him. At the time, I was six years old.

I doubt his childhood had much love, which is partly why the flat always changed for the worse with him in it. His anger hung over us, waiting to erupt. Sundays were the worst, because on Sundays there was never any work. I can still go back over forty years and remember being that little girl.

"Your da's here," I can hear my mother say.

But we would always know that; his anger seeped through the cracks in the door long before he turned the key. She cooked corned beef and cabbage on Sundays. If I try, I can still hear the cups on the dresser rattle as the door closes coffin-like behind him. The air feels threatening, my sister, brother and I sitting like unwanted additions, hoping we might somehow drift into the faded flowery wallpaper of the small front room.

His eyes would speak first, angry. No dinner yet, no plate filled, no place set. I would watch him untie his boots, his big strong hands with nails of ingrained dirt and lines that mirrored a rugged, ragged face. The steaming pot would be billowing smoke signals from the scullery, smelling of York cabbage and boiled meat. We would wait. We didn't eat; him first, always first. Through the corner of my eye, I would watch him cut the meat. Then the blind raging anger hovering since the moment he turned the key would release itself, and the plate with corned beef and cabbage would go flying through the air.

My mother would say nothing. It was best not to, not when he was like that, and not ever. I remember how the door would slam shut, and he would be gone, leaving us as castoffs in his broken wake. We would sit in silence – in case he might come back – bruised that way only children know. Today, older, I see the man differently. In part, I can carry his pain as he drowned his sorrow with Arthur Guinness, as he walked the tenement streets, as he faced his family, the anger of his failures weighing heavy on his shoulders. In some ways I am with him as he fires that plate with corned beef and lame cabbage and I can see a life as shattered as the willow pattern on that broken plate.

If I was a child again, I'd turn to my little girl self when she was sad and scared. I would reach down and gently take her by the hand. I would tell her none of it was because of her, and she will be okay. I would want to take her to a place where the anger is no more. I have that place now.

In part her sadness has made me who I am. I still feel her pain and the feelings of isolation and shame, but there was respite too. It was found in the imagination, and the love within the anger and loss. If I was a child again, I would know that there is always light within the dark.

Born in Dublin, Louise Phillips' work has been published as part of many anthologies, including *County Lines* from New Island, and various literary journals. In 2009, she won the Jonathan Swift Award for her short story "Last Kiss", and in 2011 she was a winner in the Irish Writers' Centre Lonely Voice platform. She has also been short-listed for the Molly Keane Memorial Award, Bridport UK, and long-listed twice for the *RTÉ Guide*/Penguin Short Story Competition. In 2012, she was awarded an Arts Bursary for Literature from South Dublin County Council. Her bestselling debut crime novel, *Red Ribbons*, was shortlisted for Best Irish Crime Novel of the Year (2012) in the Bord Gáis Energy Irish Book Awards. Her second novel *The Doll's House* was published August 2013. For more information, go to www.louise-phillips.com.

Dear Mam . . .

Margaret Scott

In 2004 two monumental things happened in my life. I got married and moved out of home for the first time, and six months later my mother sadly passed away. There's not a day goes by that I don't think of her, especially since I had my own two little girls. In this open letter I'd like to confess that some thirty odd years later, I guess there was method in her madness after all . . .

Dear Mam,

It is possible to have too many pets. Four dogs, two cats, a rabbit, two donkeys and a pony all seemed like a good idea at the time. Less so when they all line up to be fed. Twice a day. If the cats could call a truce and stop their middle-of-the-night altercations it would help. It's also a bit of a nuisance that one of the cats can open doors, which then enables the dog to noisily tap his way across our bedroom floor. And who'd have thought a rabbit could be so grumpy and ungrateful? I thought of you recently as I picked dandelions for him in the pouring rain under a golf umbrella. We had two rabbits and six guinea pigs at one stage when I was small. That was in addition to the seven cats,

261

five dogs and poultry too numerous to mention. How did you do it? And why?

There's an ongoing campaign in our house now for a goldfish. I wish I could ask you why you stopped short at fish – is there something I should know? Was it that they're not cuddly? Or the inevitable trauma when they're found floating upside-down in the bowl? Because that's the thing with pets, they don't live as long as we do. We buried so many pets over the years that in centuries' time they'll excavate our garden and exclaim with glee that they've stumbled across the remains of a small zoo. I can still remember how much I cried when our Yorkshire Terrier, Pip, died, and how you tried to comfort me. I thought I'd never cry like that again. But I did, though not until many years later . . .

The pony I wanted to keep in the garden was another issue. You stood firm on that one too. And boy, did I put in a long and vociferous campaign. I ranted and railed, even going so far as to draw up plans on how the henhouse could easily convert to accommodate a small 13.2 hands high Welsh Mountain Pony. But the answer was no and it stayed no. I didn't appreciate it then but that "no" did me a huge favour. When I eventually realised you meant business I started to make up stories of how I did have a pony in the henhouse. As the weeks went on that henhouse got bigger and bigger until at last Craddoxtown Stud was born and the stories became so complicated that they had to be written down. And sure the rest is history . . . I have a real pony now, you know, and you were right, the henhouse probably wouldn't have worked so well. And yes, they cost a fortune to feed.

On the subject of feeding, I now know that it was not only entirely reasonable but also totally practical to have set dinners on set days. Many's the time I complained about Bacon and Cabbage Wednesday but it's now time to confess that it's still alive and well in this house. Oh yes, right there with Leftover Monday, Stirfry Tuesday, Pasta Thursday and Whatever-you-like-I'm-wrecked Friday. And actually back when we were small, hungry, demanding children, there wasn't even the pasta option.

I'm not sure if it was simply not available or just viewed as foreign and new-fangled, but I can still remember the first time you discovered spaghetti: it was like Columbus getting his first peek of the American shoreline. It rapidly replaced Liver and Turnip Thursday and in some weeks staged a hostile takeover of Pork Chop Tuesday too.

Is it too late now to say I feel your pain? That there's nothing I'd like to do more than roll my eyes and say, "Mam, give us an idea for dinner this evening would you?" Because there is no doubt but that the "What are we having for dinner?" question struck as much fear into your heart as it does mine, topped only by "My tummy feels funny" or the dreaded "I had a bad dream, can I come into your bed?"

Which brings me nicely to sleep issues. I remember objecting strongly to going to bed one night. I'd say I was about six or seven. Anyhow, eventually you turned to me and said "I don't care if you're not tired. You don't go to bed early for you, you go to bed early for me." In recent years the fatigue that must have been behind those words has become only too clear to me. Bedtime in our house is a full hour of mayhem. And I try to do everything the books say. I try to start early, and wind them down with stories and soft music. But inevitably it degenerates into a situation where the oldest girl is screaming for one more chapter whilst the youngest, who is now the grand age of four, does laps of the house with no clothes on. That same four-year-old has only just started sleeping through the night. Four years of waking twice or three times a night can do awful things to your will to live. Is it any wonder she's the youngest? I think I was a good sleeper – I only remember venturing out of bed for the occasional bad dream, but then maybe you were just better at handling the situation than I am. You had four of us to get to bed. Who was the mad one in our house?

Frantic bedtimes aside, at least my girls are small enough for me to know exactly where they are every moment of every day. And I still worry. I never imagined the worry that came with having children. It starts from the moment you know they exist and I'm starting to doubt that it ever goes away. It now makes perfect sense that I was grounded for most of my teenage years. Don't get me wrong, by today's standards I was an angel, but it's tomorrow's standards that frighten me. I've tried not to think too far down the line, but lately the stories I've heard of what faces our teenagers make my blood run cold. There is a horrible world out there for people who want to be part of the "gang" or who are prepared to do anything to be just like everyone else. You taught us that it was okay to dance to our own beat. That we wouldn't jump into the fire if Mary down the road told us to, so why would we want to do anything else she recommended? I try to instil this sense of self-belief and self-worth into my two. But it's so hard to do that without allowing them to walk all over me. So I try instead to pick my battles. I let them pick their own clothes to wear at weekends with the only stipulation being that they're warm leaving the house and in no way resemble Rhianna's little sister. If the selection includes a fireman's outfit or a tutu, that's okay too. It'd be boring if we were all the same, I tell them. Now, it's not all plain sailing, let me assure you. I shot down a request for a television in their bedroom lately only to be met with a whine of "but everyone else has one". So I sat them down and explained that it would save them a lot of hassle down the line if they accepted right now that what "everyone else" does or has will never affect a decision I make for them.

And if none of this works? Well, I've also warned them not to go making any plans for those years between thirteen and twenty-two . . .

You were right to make me read by the way. And to read well. *Anne of Green Gables*, *The Secret Garden*, *The Pilgrim's Progress* – they were all your suggestions and I now read them to my girls. You even bought me *Gone With the Wind* when I was a teenager; and we didn't know it then, but discovering that heroines could be feisty, determined and ruthless when it came to getting their own way would come in very handy one day. My six-year-old loves to read, and I wonder if the day is coming when she too will try to sneak another chapter under the covers with a torch. I hope it is. I have all the books we read together ready for her . . .

As children, when we weren't reading we were drawing and painting and you'll be pleased to know this tradition is still going strong too. I'm not sure if the youngest is actually gifted or if it's just another vehicle for her to drive me crazy, but arts and crafts is very definitely her thing. Drawing or painting was always the remedy for boredom in our house. Every Christmas without fail we all each got a brand-new sketchpad and whatever colouring materials were most appropriate to our age, for some reason the little boxes of Flying Eagle crayons being the ones I remember most.

I can remember practically every Santa present I ever received, not because they were few in nature but because each one was *exactly* what I wanted – whether I realised it or not. I only appreciate now how much planning a Santa of that magnitude must have taken and how, on a limited budget as surely yours was, the purchasing must have been ongoing all year round. Each Santa present arrived wrapped too, with a typed label, and when people laugh at me now for wrapping Santa, I just tell them that that's the way I was taught. It adds to the wonder and the excitement and sure isn't that what it's all about?

But Christmas didn't just stop with crayons and sketchpads. It was an event that took months of planning. From September the first of the mince pies would start to appear in the kitchen and vast basins of pudding mix sat waiting for the magic stir. And even that last Christmas, when nothing was as it should be and we floundered in a state of terror and disbelief, you got me to take out a notebook and you made me write down how to cook a turkey. The day before Christmas Eve you decided to leave us to it and whilst the rest of that whole holiday was a sea of chaos and grief, the turkey was cooked and we ate it as if you were still sitting there with us.

Which brings me to one final point. I really need to say thanks for making me enter all those school writing competitions and for sitting up with me, night after night as we tweaked poems into the wee hours. Okay, it took a while for it all to pay off, but I've written a book, Mammy, a real live book. One that I think you'd enjoy (not too much B.E.D. as you used to say). But then, of course, you know all that. I could feel you there with me, into the wee hours as we tweaked it line by line. Well, don't go anywhere, apparently we have to do it again . . .

Missing you so much,

Margaret x

M argaret Scott lives in Kildare with her husband Keith Darcy, two little girls Isabelle and Emily, four dogs, two cats, two donkeys, a pony and a rabbit. An accountant by day, she recently fulfilled a lifelong dream of being a published author and her first book *Between You and Me* (published by Poolbeg Press) enjoyed several weeks in the ROI top ten bestsellers list. Margaret's writing focuses mainly on the trials and tribulations of family life and she is currently working on her second novel.

Front Page News

Áine Toner

O nly children can come in for a lot of stick – you're selfish,
you're spoilt, you get everything you want whether you
deserve it or not. But your parents think you're wicked, in the
cool, hip-to-the-groove kind of way. You get *masses* of
Christmas presents and Santa's struggling under the weight of
his gift sack – all of which is for you. And for the lucky ones,
some of that's true.

Yes, only child Áine did get away with feeding the local
pigeons with the next day's lamb dinner. Yes, there were no
recriminations when I dyed my hair bright red with permanent
marker (more on markers later). Yes, I did get away with making
a not insignificant hole in my bedroom wall (not discovered until
my parents were selling our house, erm, twenty years later) . . .
but my only-child experience was by the book, literally.

We are a bookish family; my parents adore reading and
there's always a pile of library books sitting on one of the several
mahogany tables decorating our living room (my mother likes
tables, my father likes mahogany, they won't admit it, but they
do). Sundays aren't complete without my father getting his
serious broadsheet to read commentators' analysis of the world's

biggest headlines – and me oogling the designer whatnots on the fashion and beauty pages. Growing up, I had books for the bath, for my pram, for bedtime and virtually everything in between. When I wasn't reading or being read to, I was upping my penmanship, not quite the way you'd imagine . . .

I had a penchant for tattooing my dolls with Biros as a child so perhaps a career in writing wasn't so startling. I don't think my Tiny Tears ever recovered from the number of hearts and arrows branded upon her teeny plastic person (and who would have thought pen was so difficult to remove?), and don't even mention the inked Barbies, all neatly lined up for their unwanted yet destined appointment in Áine's Tattoo Parlour. Mind you, tattooed TT was still able to wee, as my soaked father could attest.

It wasn't all personalising my toys – I used to love creating books of pictures and writing, using the 'good' stationery usually reserved for letters of complaint and as many of my father's permanent markers pilfered from work as possible. Permanent markers were something of a luxury in Belfast; you were the belle of the playground if you had one – if they got as far as the playground and you hadn't tried to dye your hair with them.

I used to present these booklets frequently. My mother still has the *This is Your Life* booklet created by her one and only for some special occasion. The opening line, *"You were born my mummy"*, never ceases to make her laugh. And I know she has a curled-up faded piece of paper in her purse with the lines, *"I love you, Mummy, I like you, Mummy"* that I devised circa 1986.

There was also the Great Complaint Letter of 1988 when seven-year-old Miss Toner gave out yards to a local theatre about a production of *Postman Pat* and the overuse of dry ice (I doubt I knew the term "dry ice" – "smoke" was probably my word of choice). Sadly, or fortunately, the missive never reached the office – so vehement was my delivery.

Artwork and annoyance aside, my childhood was dominated

by homework. Let me explain before you think I was that nerdy kid in school who didn't have any friends while the cool pupils swanned about kissing boys and pretending they were in *Jem and the Holograms* (it was 1980s Belfast, there wasn't a lot going on).

Okay, I *was* a nerdy kid in school, I have the photographs to prove it, bedecked as I was in skirts, blouses, Teenage Mutant Ninja Turtles comedy slippers (I didn't wear jeans until I was about eighteen) and Deirdre Barlowesque glasses. I loved school; I was the kind of person who'd rewrite their copy if there was one teeny tiny error. I relished starting a new copybook and the thrill of a fancy pencil case at the beginning of each academic year. Okay, term – I was quite spoilt.

I realise I'm not exactly selling myself here but bear with me. One of the best parts of my day was getting home, having my tea in front of the telly (usually *Button Moon* or *The Raggy Dolls*), eating half my father's dinner when he came home and Doing My Homework. This was a big deal; most of it would have been done by the time he'd arrive home but I always believed in sharing the load.

Obviously homework changes as you get older – it becomes more taxing, it makes you think more and you have to be more imaginative. This is where my parents stepped in, willingly I like to believe.

For, ooh, fourteen years, they helped me every single night with my essays, questions and spellings. If I needed a sentence wherein I could use the word "fluorescent", they would provide it. If I couldn't understand the relevance of working out the angle of a bucket hanging on a ladder positioned against a wall, they would at least help me with the equation. No homework task was too big or too small and I felt guided and encouraged by them every single step of the way.

This help included the Dreaded Oral Questions whereby they asked their increasingly irritable daughter common queries like where the nearest cinema was and how much a Black Forest Gateau costs.

This may sound like a childhood akin to an Enid Blyton novel. However, I am not the most patient person by nature so I can only apologise for my lack of, er, manners when their pronunciation wasn't one hundred per cent correct and I ranted at them. Yes, I know they were doing me a favour but the teenage me didn't really see that – I wanted to sound like a true native of Hamburg. If aforementioned Hamburger came from Northern Ireland.

But they gritted their teeth and stuck with me – because they could see the light at the end of the homework tunnel even if their daughter couldn't. When they hadn't read the course English texts and I needed assistance with a tricky essay, they sourced information and nodded wisely when I read out my magnum opus. They offered opinions on authors they'd never read, discussed historical events as though witnessed on an episode of *EastEnders* and generally tried to make life easier for their studious daughter.

Because they never told me I could be anything other than front page news – writing it obviously – there was already enough bad stuff happening in our city for me to add to it. When I said, aged eight, that I wanted to be a journalist, there was no going back – and there never has been.

My parents have been unreservedly my life's cheerleaders; for attending university in Dublin despite others suggesting this wasn't a good move, for becoming a journalist despite others' opinions that I should have pursued a more "academic" career, for making that risky move back to Belfast, for making that risky move back to Dublin and for becoming a magazine editor.

If, in my younger days, I had expressed an interest in being the next Beyoncé (or Belinda Carlisle – she was my icon, aged nine), they would have moved musical heaven and earth until I reached Number One. Fortunately for Beyoncé and Belinda Carlisle, I can't hold a note so there was never any chance of me giving either a run for their money.

It wasn't a case of it blowing smoke anywhere in particular, or saying it because it's written in *The Parents' Handbook* (there's a book in that). They genuinely believed I could achieve what I wanted – and I would, if they had anything to do with it. Moreover, they believed in giving me a chance – the very least I could do was live up to my side of the bargain.

I might have been studious but I was also bad-tempered and they resisted the urge (I'm sure) to tell me off more than once, particularly leading up to test season when Dreaded Oral Questions appeared more and more.

Incidentally, all this homework did pay off – I may never have the need to use this but I can efficiently recite the sixteen (yes, sixteen) versions of "the" in German in less than three seconds. And I like to think my parents would be sufficiently proficient in the romance languages to find their way to the nearest bus stop whether in Paris, Munich or ancient Rome.

Of course, it wasn't all grammar exercises and verb placements – we did leave the house occasionally. I wasn't chained to my desk – I didn't have a desk. I did my homework on my lap in front of the telly – unconventional you might think but doing your homework on a desk was something I watched on TV.

And I have been blessed with parents who weren't pushy – if anything, it was me always wanting to do more. They never asked any more of me than I could give and, unlike other parents, they stressed the importance of a work/life balance – good news for me because that meant the opportunity to buy shoes. And stationery – I can't lie, I still get a bit jittery around a well-packaged notebook.

If I could turn back time, I'd find my parents – not then prematurely aged by their offspring roaring at them about German verb pronunciation – and thank them for hanging in there. For not wanting to divorce me when I was a right wee madam and upset because they couldn't tell me the French for caterpillar*. For knowing that all those hours of homework would all pay off. For taking a leap of faith with me and staying by my side every single step of the way.

Most importantly, what I'll take to my children is – apart

from a love of stationery and staggeringly good footwear – the need to give them a chance at doing whatever they want. To give them the security of knowing that Mammy Áine will be backing them throughout their lives and woe betide anyone who gets in their way.

I vow never to lose my temper with my children when I'm devising a sentence using the word "nose" or working out chemical equations (despite the fact that the last time I was in a scientific laboratory another pupil's hair caught fire).

Experts say that children are sponges; they soak up their environment and slowly release that information. But I would argue that my mum and dad's minds are similarly porous; they have imbibed any relevant facts and figures that would be helpful to my life and drip-fed them to me when needed. As my knowledge of the journalism industry grew, so too did my parents'. They're now as equally well versed about print deadlines and standfirsts as any of my *Woman's Way* team.

The thing is, if you asked my parents, they'd say that they wished they were in a position to give me more – which I find hilarious since the only other thing they could have done was pretend to be me and sit the exams (which would have had major appeal in 1999).

As children, we can never imagine our parents existing in any form other than our parents. When I was little, I felt so loved and special – it was my mummy, daddy and me against the rest of the world. I still feel the same, over a decade after I completed my secondary education. I hope I can make my children understand that being front page news requires some work, but their mammy was born ready to make it happen.

* *chenille* is the French for caterpillar

Áine Toner has been editor of *Woman's Way*, Ireland's only weekly magazine for women, for five years and was previously its deputy editor. Her goal is to educate, entertain and inform the women of Ireland and she and her team strive to produce a packed and engaged magazine each week – while still having some fun. She also is the soapwatcher for TV3's *Ireland AM*, having spent a significant amount of her career writing about the fictional goings-on in Soapland. When she's not ogling all the books that come her way in the *Woman's Way* office (and sometimes hiding them from her colleagues), she's in bookshops buying them or weighing down delicate not-designed-to-carry-600-page-texts handbags with yet another new read. Áine is on Twitter where she talks about TV shows and cake – @aineltoner.

Believe in children

Barnardo's
Northern Ireland

Barnardo's Northern Ireland

Barnardo's NI is the largest charity working on behalf of children and young people in Northern Ireland. Our vision is that the lives of all children and young people should be free from poverty, abuse and discrimination. We aim to promote positive outcomes for all children in terms of their wellbeing, achievement and participation as young citizens.

Our focus is on those who are most disadvantaged, who are at risk, whose pathways in life have been fractured, and who face individual and collective adversities in their young lives that most of us will never encounter.

Barnardo's provides more than 40 local services in Northern Ireland. These services reach out, protect and support over 8,000 vulnerable and disadvantaged children, young people and their families in Northern Ireland every year. We also work in 150 schools in Northern Ireland, and have a network of 21 charity shops.

We offer support to children with disabilities; children who have been bereaved; children vulnerable to sexual exploitation; children of prisoners; young carers; young people at leaving care; ethnic minority families; and families where there is domestic violence, addiction or mental health issues.

Our range of work includes professional fostering; counselling and therapeutic support; residential and respite care; assessment and family support; community outreach, parenting and early education programmes; training for employment; and disability inclusion services.

We use the knowledge gained from our direct work with children and young people to campaign for children's rights bringing vital issues to the attention of the public and Northern Ireland Executive.

To find out more about Barnardo's NI or to help us fundraise, please contact us on 028 9067 2366 or visit www.barnardos.org.uk/northernireland.htm

Barnardos
www.barnardos.ie

Barnardos in Ireland

Barnardos goal is to make Ireland the best place in the world to be a child. Every day in 40 projects across Ireland Barnardos works with almost 6,300 children and families whose lives are marred by issues such as poverty, neglect and educational disadvantage.

We support children whose well-being is under threat, by working with them, their families and communities and by campaigning for the rights of children. For over fifty years Barnardos has worked closely with more than 100,000 children and families living in disadvantaged communities throughout Ireland, supporting them to achieve their potential in life.

The Barnardos network includes more than 40 project centres located in the heart of communities. It operates eight Early Years services, 19 Family Support programmes, five Teen Parent programmes and four Family Welfare Conference services. In addition, Barnardos provides some specialist programmes nationally such as counselling services dealing with childhood bereavement and post adoption, a Guardian ad Litem service representing children's interests in court proceedings and an information resource network for parents and childcare professionals.

Barnardos is committed to a *needs-led, outcomes-focused* approach in our delivery of services to children and families. At the heart of everything we do, we strive to achieve two outcomes for the children and young people.

These are:

- ○ *Increased emotional well-being*
- ○ *Improved learning and development*

We believe that if a child's learning and development, and his or her emotional well-being, is successfully and measurably improved through our work, then the child's ability to benefit from life opportunities and manage life challenges will be improved, and therefore the path of his or her life will be changed for the better.

For more information on Barnardos work with children and families in Ireland today please visit www.barnardos.ie